TO M.C.
I LOVE YOU
your
daughter
P. aTRICIa

THE SALVATION ARMY
SONGS OF FAITH

FOR CONGREGATIONAL SINGING

(A Supplement to The Salvation Army Song Book)

HEADQUARTERS FOR CANADA AND BERMUDA
20 Albert Street, Toronto, Ontario

ISBN 0-88857-011-2

Made and printed in Toronto, Canada

FOREWORD

Let me commend this supplement to our Salvation Army Song Book. It unites two fundamental expressions of Christian experience — the songs we sing and the faith we hold. We sing our songs because of our faith. Our faith is in Jesus Christ who died to redeem us; and our songs are about Him and the blessings and benefits unloosed upon the world through his dying.

May Salvationists of Canada and Bermuda ever remain close to their Lord with the jubilant songs on their lips and the compassion of Christ in their hearts.

(C.D. Wiseman)
Commissioner
Territorial Commander

EDITOR'S NOTE

This song book includes many old favourites not hitherto published by The Salvation Army specifically for congregational singing. The opportunity has been taken to include songs which have become popular since their appearance in The Musical Salvationist, and others not previously published.

The harmonies in this vocal setting will be found to agree with those of the companion Band arrangements. The keys also agree with the Band arrangements, except in certain cases where the exact agreement would involve remote keys in the Band arrangements. In these cases, the key that corresponds with that of the Band arrangement is shown, in brackets, at the top of the page and involves only a substitution of flats for sharps, the notation remaining the same.

Norman Bearcroft
Music Department, 1971

NOTICE

SUBJECT INDEX

Praise and Adoration .... 1 to 16
The News of Salvation .... 17 to 32
Experience and Testimony .... 33 to 51
Consecration and Service .... 52 to 73
Faith and Trust .... 74 to 91
The Salvation War .... 92 to 99

1 - Joyful, Joyful, We Adore Thee

BEETHOVEN
from the Ninth Symphony

(Gb) Maestoso ♩ = 72

1. Joy - ful, joy - ful, we a - dore Thee, God of glo - ry, Lord of love;

Hearts un - fold like flow'rs be - fore Thee, Hail Thee as the sun a - bove.

Melt the clouds of sin and sad - ness, Drive the dark of doubt a - way;

Giv - er of im - mor - tal glad - ness, Fill us with the light of day!

2. All Thy works with joy surround Thee,
   Earth and heaven reflect Thy rays,
Stars and angels sing around Thee,
   Centre of unbroken praise;
Field and forest, vale and mountain,
   Bloss'ming meadow, flashing sea,
Chanting bird and flowing fountain
   Call us to rejoice in Thee.

3. Thou art giving and forgiving,
   Ever blessing, ever blest,
Well-spring of the joy of living,
   Ocean-depth of happy rest!
Thou the Father, Christ our Brother —
   All who live in love are Thine:
Teach us how to love each other,
   Lift us to the joy divine.

4. Mortals, join the mighty chorus
   Which the morning stars began;
Father-love is reigning o'er us,
   Brother-love binds man to man.
Ever singing, march we onward,
   Victors in the midst of strife;
Joyful music lifts us sunward
   In the triumph song of life.

Henry van Dyke

2 - For Thine is the Kingdom

JOHN GOWANS

JOHN LARSSON

Maestoso ♩ = 76

For Thine is the King-dom, and Thine is the pow'r, And
Thine __ is the glo - ry for ev - er and ev - er; For
Thine is the King - dom, And
Thine is the pow'r, And

Thine _____ is the glo - ry for

ev - er and ev - er;

For ev - er and ev - er, A - men.

3 - I Will Sing of My Redeemer

Blood _____ He pur - chased me _____ On ___ the
Blood, with His Blood, He pur - chased me, He pur - chased me, On the

cross _____ He sealed my par - don. Paid ___ the
cross, on the cross He sealed my par - don, Paid the

debt _____ and made me free. _____
debt, Paid the debt and made me free, made me free.

2. I will sing the wondrous story,
   How my lost estate to save,
   In His boundless love and mercy,
   He the ransom freely gave.

3. I will praise my dear Redeemer,
   His triumphant power I'll tell;
   How the victory He giveth
   Over sin, and death, and hell.

4. I will sing of my Redeemer,
   And His heavenly love to me;
   He from death to life has brought me,
   Son of God, with Him to be.

Philip P. Bliss

4 - Beautiful Christ

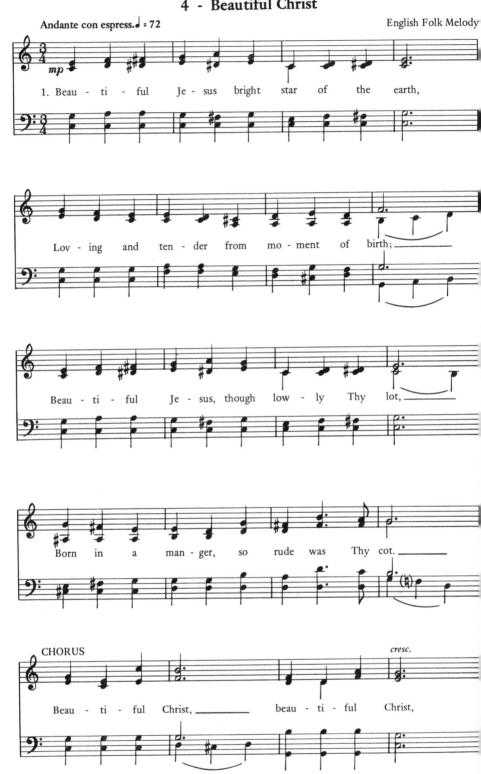

Andante con espress. ♩ = 72

English Folk Melody

1. Beau - ti - ful Je - sus bright star of the earth,

Lov - ing and ten - der from mo - ment of birth;____

Beau - ti - ful Je - sus, though low - ly Thy lot,____

Born in a man - ger, so rude was Thy cot.____

CHORUS

cresc.

Beau - ti - ful Christ, ____ beau - ti - ful Christ,

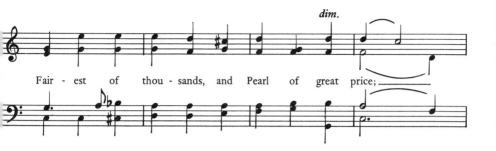

Fair - est of thou - sands, and Pearl of great price;

Beau - ti - ful Christ, _____ beau - ti - ful Christ,

Glad - ly we wel - come Thee, beau - ti - ful Christ.

2. Beautiful Jesus, what treasure you brought,
When from heav'n's splendour the earth first You sought!
Beautiful Jesus, beloved of God,
Emblem of purity, Emblem of good!

3. Beautiful Jesus, so gentle and mild;
Light of the sinner in ways dark and wild;
Beautiful Jesus, oh, save such just now,
As at Thy feet they in penitence bow!

Mrs. Ashby

5 - Great is Thy Faithfulness

Moderato ♩ = 92

WILLIAM M. RUNYAN

1."Great is Thy faith-ful-ness", O God my Fa-ther, There is no sha-dow of turn-ing with Thee; Thou chang-est not, Thy com-pas-sions, they fail not; As Thou hast been Thou for-e-ver wilt be.

CHORUS
mf *cresc.*

"Great is Thy faith-ful-ness! Great is Thy faith-ful-ness!" Morn-ing by morn-ing new mer-cies I see; All I have need-ed Thy hand hath pro-vid-ed, "Great is Thy faith-ful-ness," Lord, un-to me!

rall. e dim.

2. Summer and winter, and springtime and harvest,
Sun, moon, and stars in their courses above,
Join with all nature in manifold witness
To Thy great faithfulness, mercy, and love.

3. Pardon for sin and a peace that endureth,
Thy own dear presence to cheer and to guide,
Strength for today and bright hope for tomorrow,
Blessings all mine, with ten thousand beside!

T. O. Chisholm

6 - May Jesus Christ Be Praised

SIR JOSEPH BARNBY

Maestoso ♩ = 92

1. When morn-ing gilds the skies, ____ My heart a-wak-'ning cries, ____ May
Je - sus Christ be praised: A - like at work and prayer ____ To
Je - sus I re - pair; ____ May Je - sus Christ be praised.

2. Does sadness fill my mind?
   A solace here I find,
       May Jesus Christ be praised:
   Or fades my earthly bliss?
   My comfort still is this,
       May Jesus Christ be praised.

3. The night becomes as day,
   When from the heart we say,
       May Jesus Christ be praised:
   The powers of darkness fear,
   When this sweet chant they hear,
       May Jesus Christ be praised.

4. To God, the Word, on high,
   The hosts of angels cry;
       May Jesus Christ be praised:
   Let mortals, too, upraise
   Their voice in hymns of praise;
       May Jesus Christ be praised.

5. In heav'n's eternal bliss
   The loveliest strain is this,
       May Jesus Christ be praised:
   Let earth, and sea, and sky
   From depth to height reply
       May Jesus Christ be praised.

Trans. from German
by E. Caswell

7 - Not Unto Us, O Lord

Maestoso ♩ = 92

Tune: St. John

1. Not un - to us O Lord, But un - to Thy Great name; Our trum - pets are a - wake, Our ban - ners are a - flame. We boast no bat - tle ev - er won; The vic - to - ry is Thine a - lone.

2. We were that foolish thing
   Unversed in worldly ways,
   Which Thou didst choose and use
   Unto Thy greater praise.
   Called and commissioned from afar
   To bring to nought the things that are.

3. A hundred anthems rise
   For ev'ry fighting year,
   Since Thou, as Lord of Hosts,
   Our Captain did appear
   To sanctify, to take command
   And bring us to our Promised Land.

4. Not yet we hail the day
   When all to Thee shall yield,
   But we behold Thee stand
   Upon our battle-field.
   And this alone shall ever be
   Our sign and seal of victory.

Albert Orsborn

(Written for the Salvation Army Centenary 1865-1965)

8 - Thanksgiving

ALBERT DALZIEL

Maestoso ♩ = 92

1. Where-in shall a na-tion glo-ry, And to whom her tri-butes pay?

In her high day of re-mem-brance, Where her laur-els just-ly lay?

Un-to Thee, O God, the glo-ry, Un-to Thee be high-est praise,

Who in mer-cy has sus-tained her, Ev-er through the length of days.

2. It is timely for a people
   To acknowledge and acclaim,
Worthy men and great occasions
   Adding lustre to her name;
Through the annals of a century
   We can trace her checkered road,
And with thankful hearts and humble,
   Mark the providence of God.

3. Blest indeed are men and nations
   Who their heritage received
From the sturdy faith of forbears
   Living out what they believed;
They, with Godly fear and toiling
   Raised a people strong and free,
Grant, O God, that no despoiling
   Of this heritage shall be.

4. Of her bounty without measure,
   On this land has nature poured,
Beauty, plenty, far-spread acres,
   Dormant treasures deeply stored.
May we, by our just dividing,
   Seek the greatest common good,
Knowing that these gifts unsparing
   Bear the signature of God.

5. Not alone by man's devices
   Are his greatest triumphs won,
Nor alone from man's resources,
   Is a new-born world begun.
Wellspring of all man's requiring
   May, O God, we learn at length,
Righteousness exalts a nation
   And in virtue is her strength.

(Written for Canadian Centennial Celebrations 1867-1967)   *Albert Dalziel*

9 - Praise Him! Praise Him!

Allegro ♩. = 96

CHESTER G. ALLEN

1. Praise Him! Praise Him! Je - sus our bless - ed Re - deem - er!

Sing, O earth, His won - der - ful love pro - claim! ____

Hail Him! Hail Him! high - est arch - ang - els In glo - ry;

Strength and hon - our give to His ho - ly name! ____

Like a shep - herd, Je - sus will guard His child - ren,

In His arms He car - ries them all day long;

CHORUS

Praise Him! Praise Him! tell of His ex - cel - lent great - ness;

Praise Him! Praise Him! ev - er in joy - ful song!

2. Praise Him! Praise Him!
    Jesus, our blessed Redeemer!
  For our sins He suffered, and bled, and died;
    He our Rock, our hope of eternal salvation,
  Hail Him! Hail Him! Jesus, the Crucified!
    Sound His praises, Jesus who bore our sorrows,
  Love unbounded, wonderful, deep, and strong;

3. Praise Him! Praise Him!
    Jesus, our blessed Redeemer!
  Heav'nly portals, loud with hosannas ring!
    Jesus, Saviour, reigneth for ever and ever:
  Crown Him! Crown Him! Prophet, and Priest, and King!
    Christ is coming, over the world victorious,
  Pow'r and glory unto the Lord belong;

Fanny J. Crosby

10 - The Fairest of Ten Thousand

Moderato ♩ = 69

L. J. ROWLANDS

1. O Thou fair - est of ten thou - sand, How my heart goes out to Thee!

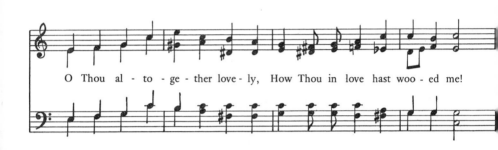

O Thou al - to - ge - ther love - ly, How Thou in love hast woo - ed me!

cresc.

With Thy cross of bit - ter sor - row, With Thy pas - sion, with Thy blood,

dim.

Thou hast won me, Thou hast con - quer'd, O Thou all - re - deem - ing Lord!

CHORUS

Moderato ♪ = 120

At Thy feet I bow, a - dor - ing; Bend-ing low - er, low - er still;

Giv - ing up my all to fol - low, Just to do my Mas - ter's will.

Giv - ing up my all to fol - low, Just to do my Mas - ter's will.

2. Oh, the sweetness of true living,
    Covered with Thy gracious smile!
Oh, the purity of purpose
    Thou dost teach my heart the while!
Oh, the longings to be fruitful,
    Winning many for Thy cross;
Walking with Thee, it is heaven,
    While earth's pleasures seem as dross.

Susie Barker

11 - The God of Abraham Praise

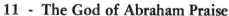

Maestoso ♩ = 72

Hebrew Tune "Leoni"

1. The God of Abraham praise, Who reigns en-throned a-bove, An-
cient of e-ver-last-ing days, And God of_ Love. Je-
ho-vah, Great I am,____ By earth and heaven con-
fest; I bow and bless the sa-cred Name For-e-ver blest.

2. The God of Abraham praise,
  At whose supreme command
From earth I rise, and seek the joys
  At His right hand:
I all on earth forsake,
  Its wisdom, fame, and power;
And Him my only portion make,
  My shield and tower.

3. Before the Saviour's face
  The ransomed nations bow,
O'erwhelmed at His almighty grace
  For ever new;
He shows His prints of love,
  They kindle to a flame!
And sound through all the worlds above
  "Worthy the Lamb".

4. He by Himself hath sworn,
  I on His oath depend,
I shall, on eagle's wings upborne,
  To heaven ascend:
I shall behold His face,
  I shall His power adore,
And sing the wonders of His grace
  For evermore!

5. The whole triumphant host
  Give thanks to God on high;
"Hail! Father, Son, and Holy Ghost,"
  They ever cry:
Hail, Abraham's God and mine;
  I join the heavenly lays;
All might and majesty are Thine,
  And endless praise!

Thomas Olivers

12 - The Name of Jesus

Andante ♩ = 72

E. S. LORENZ

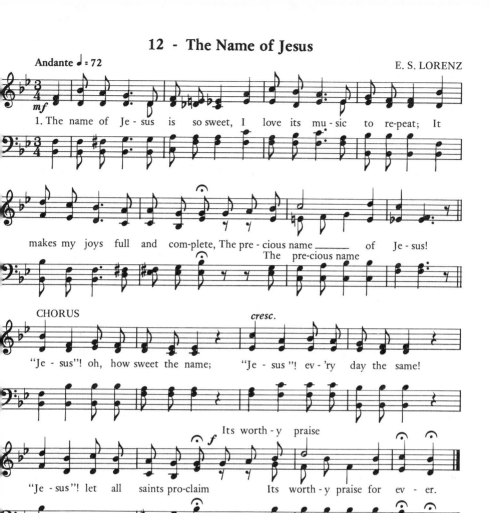

1. The name of Je - sus is so sweet, I love its mu - sic to re-peat; It makes my joys full and com-plete, The pre - cious name _____ of Je - sus! The pre-cious name

CHORUS *cresc.*

"Je - sus"! oh, how sweet the name; "Je - sus"! ev - 'ry day the same!

f Its worth - y praise

"Je - sus"! let all saints pro-claim Its worth - y praise for ev - er.

2. I love the name of Him whose heart
   Knows all my griefs and bears my part;
   Who bids all anxious fears depart,
   I love the name of Jesus!

3. That name I fondly love to hear,
   It never fails my heart to cheer,
   Its music dries the falling tear:
   Exalt the name of Jesus!

4. No word of man can ever tell
   How sweet the name I love so well;
   Oh, let its praises ever swell!
   Oh, praise the name of Jesus!

W. C. Martin

13 - Thine is the Glory

Maestoso ♩ = 72

HANDEL

mf

1. Thine is the glo-ry, Ris-en, con-qu'ring Son; End-less is the

vic-t'ry Thou o'er death hast won. An-gels in bright rai-ment

Rolled the stone a-way, Kept the fold-ed grave-clothes

CHORUS

ff

Where Thy bod-y lay. Thine is the glo-ry, Ris-en, con-qu'ring Son;

End-less is the vic-t'ry Thou o'er death hast won.

2. Lo! Jesus meets thee,
   Risen from the tomb;
   Lovingly He greets thee,
   Scatters fear and gloom;
   Let His church with gladness
   Hymns of triumph sing,
   For her Lord now liveth;
   Death hath lost its sting.

3. No more we doubt Thee,
   Glorious Prince of Life!
   Life is nought without Thee;
   Aid us in our strife;
   Make us more than conquerors
   Through Thy deathless love;
   Bring us safe through Jordan
   To Thy home above.

Edmond Budry
trans. by R. Birch Hoyle

14 - This is my Father's World

Moderato ♩ = 100   Terra Beata   FRANKLIN L. SHEPPARD

1. This is my Fa - ther's world, And to my list - ening ears All
na - ture sings and round me rings The mu - sic of the spheres. This
is my Fa - ther's world, I rest me in the thought of
rocks and trees, of skies and seas; His hand the won - ders wrought.

2. This is my Father's world:
   The birds their carols raise,
   The morning light, the lily white,
   Declare their Maker's praise.
   This is my Father's world:
   He shines in all that's fair;
   In the rustling grass, I hear Him pass,
   He speaks to me ev'ry where.

3. This is my Father's world:
   O, let me ne'er forget
   That though the wrong seems oft so strong,
   God is the Ruler yet.
   This is my Father's world:
   The battle is not done;
   Jesus who died shall be satisfied,
   And earth and heav'n be one.

Maltbie D. Babcock

15 - We Gather Together

(Db)

Andante ♩ = 100

NETHERLANDS FOLK SONG

1. We gath - er to - geth - er to ask the Lord's bless - ing; He
chas - tens and has - tens His will to make known; The
wick - ed op - press - ing now cease___ from dis - tress - ing, Sing
prais - es to His Name;___ He for - gets not His own.

2. Beside us to guide us, our God with us joining,
   Ordaining, maintaining His kingdom divine;
   So from the beginning the fight we are winning,
   Thou, Lord, wast at our side, all glory be Thine.

3. We do all extol Thee, Thou Leader triumphant,
   And pray that Thou still our Defender wilt be;
   Let Thy congregation escape tribulation:
   Thy name be ever praised! O Lord, make us free.

Trs. Theodore Baker

16 - We Worship Thee, O Lord of Light

Andante ♩ = 90

Netherlands Melody

mf

1. We wor - ship Thee O Lord of Light, And in Thy pre - sence bow; For all the to - kens of Thy Light, We give Thee glo - ry now. Thy ways we may not un - der - stand, But while the plan is in Thy hand, We ask not more to know.

cresc.

dim.

2. Blessed Interpreter of all
   Divine and holy thought,
   Hear us, O hear us, when we call,
   Father, forbid us not.
   We feel the yearning of desire,
   O stir this gently burning fire
   Into a ceaseless glow.

3. We crave to reach that gracious height
   Where holy men have trod;
   The Palace of the Infinite
   The Treasure House of God.
   Thy love has made our eyes to see,
   Our love is kindling after Thee,
   In us Thy beauty show.

Albert Orsborn

17 - A Mighty Fortress
(Ein Feste Burg)

(Db) Maestoso ♩ = 60

MARTIN LUTHER

1. A migh-ty fort - ress is our God, A bul-wark ne - ver fail - ing;
Our help-er He, a - mid the flood, Of mor-tal ills pre - vail - ing.

For still our an - cient foe Doth seek to work us woe; His craft and pow'r are

great, And, armed with cru - el hate, On earth is not His e - qual.

2. Did we in our own strength confide,
   Our striving would be losing;
   Were not the right Man on our side,
   The Man of God's own choosing.
   Dost ask who that may be?
   Christ Jesus, it is He;
   Lord Sabaoth His name,
   From age to age the same,
   And He must win the battle.

3. And though this world, with demons filled,
   Should threaten to undo us;
   We will not fear, for God hath willed
   His truth to triumph through us.
   The Prince of darkness grim,
   We tremble not for him,
   His rage we can endure,
   For lo! his doom is sure,
   One little word shall fell him.

4. That word above all earthly powers,
   No thanks to them, abideth;
   The Spirit and the gifts are ours
   Through Him who with us sideth.
   Let goods and kindred go,
   This mortal life also;
   The body they may kill;
   God's truth abideth still,
   His kingdom is for ever.

Martin Luther
Trans. Frederick H. Hedge

18 - Arise, My Soul, Arise

Tune: Lenox

1. A - rise, my soul, a - rise, Shake off thy guil - ty fears; The bleed - ing Sac - ri - fice In my be - half ap - pears; Be - fore the Throne my sure - ty stands, my name is writ - ten on His hands, My name is writ - ten on His hands.

2. He ever lives above
    For me to intercede,
His all-redeeming love,
    His precious Blood to plead;
His Blood atoned for all our race,
    And sprinkles now the throne of grace.

3. Five bleeding wounds He bears,
    Received on Calvary;
They pour effectual prayers,
    They strongly plead for me.
Forgive him, O forgive, they cry,
    Nor let that ransomed sinner die.

4. The Father hears Him pray,
    His dear Anointed One ;
He cannot turn away
    The presence of His Son:
His spirit answers to the Blood
    And tells me I am born of God.

5. My God is reconciled,
    His pardoning voice I hear ;
He owns me for His child,
    I can no longer fear;
With confidence I now draw nigh
    And Father, Abba Father! cry.

Charles Wesley

19 - At Calvary

Moderato ♩ = 86

D. B. TOWNER

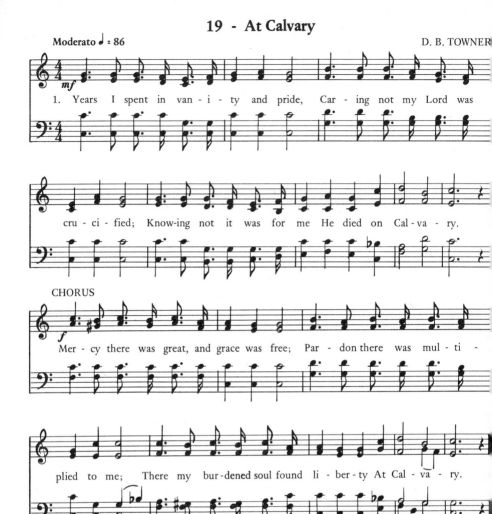

1. Years I spent in van-i-ty and pride, Car-ing not my Lord was cru-ci-fied; Know-ing not it was for me He died on Cal-va-ry.

CHORUS

Mer-cy there was great, and grace was free; Par-don there was mul-ti-plied to me; There my bur-dened soul found li-ber-ty At Cal-va-ry.

2. By God's word at last my sin I learned,
   Then I trembled at the law I'd spurned,
   Till my guilty soul imploring turned
   To Calvary.

3. Now I've giv'n to Jesus ev'rything,
   Now I gladly own Him as my King;
   Now my raptured soul can only sing
   Of Calvary.

4. Oh, the love that drew salvation's plan!
   Oh, the love that brought it down to man!
   Oh, the mighty gulf that God did span
   At Calvary!

Wm. R. Newell

20 - He Came Right Down to Me

Andante moderato ♩ = 70

B. D. ACKLEY

mp

1. When won-drous words my Lord would say, That I un-to His mind may

cresc.   *f*

reach, He choos-es out a low-ly way, And robes His thoughts in child-like speech.

CHORUS *mf*

He came right down to me, He came right down to me, To con-de -

dim.

scend to be my friend, He came right down to me.

2. The Voice Divine, those accents dear
    I languished for, yet had not heard
    Till Jesus came with message clear,
        And brought to me the living word.

3. Nor could I see my Maker's face,
        Veiled from my sight His far abode,
    Till Christ made known the Father's grace,
        And shared with men their heavy load.

4. O Vision clear, O Voice Divine!
        Dear Son of God and Son of Man!
    Let all Thy gifts of grace be mine;
        Complete in me Thy perfect plan.

Albert Orsborn

21 - His Love Remains the Same

JOHN LARSSON

Moderato ♩ = 60

1.Don't as-sume that God's dis-missed you from His mind,_____
Don't as-sume that God's for-got-ten to be kind;_____
For no mat-ter what you do, His love still fol-lows
you, Don't think that you have left Him far be-hind._____

CHORUS

For His love re-mains the same, He knows you by your name, __Don

think be - cause you failed Him He des - pairs, _____ For He

gives to those who ask His grace for ev' - ry task, _____ God

plans for you in love for He still cares. _____

2. Don't assume that God will plan for you no more,
   Don't assume that there's no future to explore;
   For your life He'll re-design, the pattern be divine,
   Don't think that your repentance He'll ignore.

3. Don't assume you cannot give what He'll demand,
   Don't assume that God condemns you out of hand;
   For He gives to those who ask His grace for ev'ry task,
   Don't think that God will fail to understand.

John Gowans

22 - I Am Amazed

SIDNEY E. COX

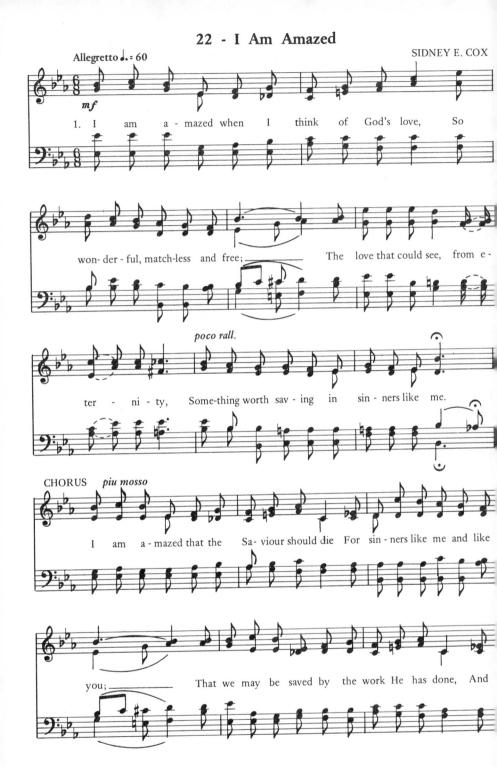

Allegretto ♩.= 60

mf

1. I am a-mazed when I think of God's love, So won-der-ful, match-less and free; The love that could see, from e-ter-ni-ty, Some-thing worth sav-ing in sin-ners like me.

CHORUS *piu mosso*

I am a-mazed that the Sa-viour should die For sin-ners like me and like you; That we may be saved by the work He has done, And

not by the works that we do. ___ But it's true, ___ it's true, ___ This

won-der-ful sto-ry so old, but so new. I am a-mazed that the

Sa-viour should die For sin-ners like me and like you.

2. I am amazed when I think of God's grace,
   O word with the heavenly sound;
   For sinners condemned, what way could be found?
   More than sufficient God's grace did abound.

3. I am amazed when I think of God's Son,
   From glory to Calv'ry He came
   To bear in my place, sin's darkness and shame;
   O what a Saviour, and Jesus His name.

Sidney E. Cox

23 - I Know a Fount

OLIVER COOK

Moderato ♩ = 72

mf

1. Say, are you wear - y? Are you hea - vy la - den?
Bur - den'd with sor - row, __ Weigh - ted down with care? __

mp *cresc.*

Are __ you in bond - age? Do you want de - liv' - rance? __

f

Come, then, with me, there is re - fuge from des - pair.

CHORUS

mf

I know a fount where __ sins are wash'd a - way,

I know a place where night is turned to day;

Bur - dens are lift - ed,___ blind eyes made to see; There's a

won - der work - ing power in the Blood of Cal - va - ry.

2. Are you still doubting power to keep from sinning,
   Power that can change the heart and make it new?
   Are you still longing for a full Salvation?
   You may receive it and live a life that's true.

3. Fetter'd and bound by chains of self - indulgence,
   Missing the blessings God on man bestows,
   Seeking for joy but only sorrow finding;
   Come to the waters where grace and mercy flow.

4. Wondrous Deliv'rer! Sin - forgiving Saviour!
   Cleanser of hearts! Unfailing Friend and Guide,
   No one has ever trusted unavailing,
   No one has claim'd of His love and been denied.

Oliver Cooke

24 - Mighty to Save

CHARLES COLLE

Joy - ful news to all man - kind,___ Je - sus is might- y to save !

All who seek shall sure - ly find___

save to save___

Je - sus is might - y to save ! Sin - ners may re -

to save

lin - quish wrong,___ Fal - t'ring hearts may now be strong,___

Sound the tid - ings right a - long,___ Je - sus is might - y (S.B.) to / (A.T.) is

f CHORUS

might - y to save! Je - sus is might - y to save!

Je - sus is might - y to save! From the ut - ter most,

To the ut - ter most, Might - y to save!

2. Though as scarlet be the stains,
    Jesus is mighty to save!
   Though as steel the binding chains,
    Jesus is mighty to save!
   His the glorious sacrifice,
   His the Blood which paid the price,
   His the love doth now entice;
    Jesus is mighty to save!

3. Fearful soul discard thy fears
    Jesus is mighty to save!
   Seeker haste to dry those tears,
    Jesus is mighty to save!
   With assurance seek His face,
   Doubt no more His love and grace,
   Give Him now His rightful place,
    Jesus is mighty to save!

4. Since His Blood for thee was shed,
    Jesus is mighty to save!
   Since He lives who once was dead,
    Jesus is mighty to save!
   While in conflict we engage,
   When the storms around shall rage,
   All our earthly pilgrimage,
    Jesus is mighty to save!

Charles Coller

25 - O Love Upon a Cross Impaled

(D♭) Moderato ♩ = 96

MOZAR...

1. O Love u-pon a cross im-paled, My con-trite heart is drawn to Thee; Are Thine the hands my pride has nailed? And Thine the sor-rows borne for me? Are such the wounds my sin de-crees? I fall in shame up-on my knees.

2. 'Twere not for sinners such as I
    To gaze upon Thy sore distress,
Or comprehend Thy bitter cry
    Of God-forsaken loneliness!
I shelter from such agonies
    Beneath Thy cross, upon my knees.

3. "Forgive! Forgive! " I hear Thee plead;
    "And me forgive! " I instant cry.
For me Thy wounds shall intercede,
    For me Thy prayer shall make reply.
I take the grace that flows from these,
    In saving faith, upon my knees.

4. Now take Thy throne, O Crucified,
    And be my love-anointed King.
The weapons of my sinful pride
    Are broken by Thy suffering!
A captive to love's victories,
    I yield, I yield upon my knees!

Albert Orsborn

Db)

26 - On Every Hill

Andante con espress ♩ = 60

Tune: "He wipes the tear".

mp

1. On ev'-ry hill our Sav-iour dies, __ And not on Calv'-rys_ height a-
lone;__ His sor-rows dark-ened all our skies,__ His griefs for

cresc.

dim. *mf* CHORUS

all our wrongs a-tone. Go! Cry the news from ev'-ry
hill. Go! Ring the earth with sa-cred flame; To par-don

cresc.

dim. *rall.*

is the Fa-ther's will,__ And Je-sus is the Sav-iour's name.

2. Present He is in all our woes,
   Upon a world-wide Cross is hung;
   And with exceeding bitter throes
   His world-embracing heart is wrung.

3. In us His love invested is,
   God cannot pass a suppliant by;
   For heard in God's eternities
   Our prayers repeat the Saviour's cry.

4. And for the sake of that dear name
   With which all hope of good is given;
   Our heavy load of sin and shame,
   The Father clears, and cries, "Forgiven!"

Albert Orsborn

27 - Sacred Hands of Jesus

J. L. MOLLO

Andante con moto ♩ = 69

cresc.

p

1. Once, on a day, was Christ led forth to die, And with the crowd that

mp cresc.

pressed on Him joined I. Slow - ly they led Him, led Him to the tree, ___

mf

And I be- held His hands were no more free! Bound fast with cords! An

dim. *rit.*

this was His dis-tress, That men de-nied those hands outstretched to bless. ___

CHORUS *a tempo*
mp

Sa - cred hands of Je - sus, they were bound for me; Wound - ed hands of

Je - sus, stretched up - on a tree,———— E - ver in - ter -
ced - ing, 'Mer - cy!' is their plea. Their ef - fect - ual
plead - ing brings grace to me, re - deem-ing grace to___ me.

2. Hands that were scarred by daily fret and tear;
   Hands quick to soothe the troubled brow of care;
   Hands strong to smite the sins that men enthrone,
   Yet never raised to seek or claim their own:
   Dear hands of Christ! and yet men feared them so,
   That they must bind them, as to death they go.

3. Hands that still break to men the Living Bread;
   Hands full of pow'r to raise again the dead,
   Potent and healing, eager to reclaim,
   Laid in forgiveness on one bowed in shame.
   Say, would'st thou bind, by pride and belief,
     Those hands that compass all thy soul's relief?

Albert Orsborn

28 - Swing Wide the Door of Your Heart

Moderato ♩. = 76

SIDNEY E. COX

1. Are you seek - ing joys that will not fade,

Last - ing plea - sure, by God's mer - cy made?

Christ is wait - ing, ful - ness of joy He brings,

Swing wide the door of your heart to the King of kings.

mf CHORUS

Swing wide the door of your heart to the King of kings, ___

Bid Him wel - come, for won - der - ful peace He brings, _____

He will shel - ter thee un - der His out - stretched wings; _____

Swing wide the door of your heart to the King of kings. _____

2. Are you longing perfect peace to win?
   Turn to Jesus, bid Him enter in;
   Peace is found but under His shelt'ring wings,
   Swing wide the door of your heart to the King of kings.

3. Now He calls you with His wondrous voice,
   Bid Him welcome, make His will your choice;
   At His coming heavenly music rings,
   Swing wide the door of your heart to the King of kings.

Sidney E. Cox

29 - The Ninety and Nine

2. "Lord, Thou hast here Thy ninety and nine;
    Are they not enough for Thee? "
But the Shepherd made answer: — "This of Mine
    Has wandered away from Me;
And, although the road be rough and steep,
    I go to the desert to find My sheep,
I go to the desert to find My sheep".

3. But none of the ransomed ever knew
    How deep were the waters crossed;
Nor how dark was the night that the Lord passed through
    Ere He found His sheep that was lost.
Out in the desert He heard its cry,
    Sick, and helpless, and ready to die,
Sick, and helpless, and ready to die.

4. "Lord, whence are those blood drops all t
    That mark out the mountain's track? "
"They were shed for one who had gone as
    Ere the Shepherd could bring him back
"Lord, whence are Thy hands so rent and
    "They are pierced tonight by many a th
They are pierced tonight by many a thorn

5. But all through the mountains, thunder ri
    And up from the rocky steep,
There arose a great cry to the gate of heav
    "Rejoice! I have found my sheep".
And the angels echoed around the throne
    "Rejoice, for the Lord brings back His
Rejoice, for the Lord brings back His owr

Elizabeth C. Clephan

30 - His Saving Power

Moderato con espress. ♩ = 112

JOHN WELLS

1. She on - ly touched the hem of His gar - ment As to His
side she stole, _____ A - mid the crowd that gath-ered a - round Him, And
straight-way she was whole. O _____ touch the hem of His gar - ment, And
thou, too, shalt be free; _____ His sav - ing pow'r, this ve - ry
hour, shall give new life to thee! _____ life to thee! _____

cresc.

rit. CHORUS *a tempo*

2. She came in fear and trembling before Him;
   She knew her Lord had come;
   She felt that from Him virtue had healed her;
   The mighty deed was done.

3. He turned with, "Daughter, be of good comfort,
   Thy faith hath made thee whole!"
   And peace that passeth all understanding
   With gladness filled her soul.

George F. Root

31 - There is Mercy in Jesus

HENRY BISHOP

Andante ♩ = 69

mp

1. You may roam thro' the world, but you'll al - ways be wea - ry, You'll

ne - ver find rest till you're par - doned by God; The

plea - sures of sin will en - snare and de - ceive you; You'll

ne - ver find rest till you're washed in the Blood. No

rest in the world where - so - e - ver you rove;___ No

rest but in Je - sus' in - fi - nite love. Though
o'er the wide world you go seek - ing for plea - sure You'll
never find rest till you're par - doned by God. There is

CHORUS

mer - cy in Je - sus, there's mer - cy in Je - sus, There's
par - don for all who will come - to the Blood.

2. Though you are an out-cast, a rebel, a sinner,
   And deeper than crimson the dye of your sin,
Come quickly to Jesus, and you'll be forgiven;
   Your Saviour, your Refuge, you'll find all in Him.
Then come to the Saviour, no longer delay,
   With arms open wide He is waiting today.
He has mercy to pardon and strength to relieve you,
He never yet turned one poor sinner away.

Anon.

(Db)

32 - These Things I Know

Andante ♩ = 60

The Londonderry Ai

mf

1. I can-not tell why He, whom an-gels wor - ship, ___ should set His
love up - on the sons of men, ___ Or why, as Shep-herd He should seek th
wan - derers, To bring them back, they know not how or when. ___ But this I
know, that He was born of Ma - ry, When Beth - lehem
man - ger was His on - ly home, ___ And that He lived at Naz - a - reth and

la - boured, And so the Sav-iour, Sav - iour of the world is come. _____

2. I cannot tell how silently He suffered,
   As with His peace He graced this place of tears,
Or how His heart upon the Cross was broken,
   The crown of pain to three and thirty years.
But this I know, He heals the broken - hearted,
   And stays our sin, and calms our lurking fear,
And lifts the burden from the heavy laden,
   For yet the Saviour, Saviour of the world, is here.

3. I cannot tell how He will win the nations,
   How He will claim His earthly heritage,
How satisfy the needs and aspirations
   Of East and West, of sinner and of sage.
But this I know, all flesh shall see His glory,
   And He shall reap the harvest He has sown,
And some glad day His sun shall shine in splenour
   When He the Saviour, Saviour of the world, is known.

4. I cannot tell how all the lands shall worship,
   When at His bidding, every storm is stilled,
Or who can say how great the jubilation
   When all the hearts of men with love are filled.
But this I know, the skies will thrill with rapture,
   And myriad, myriad human voices sing,
And earth to heaven, and heaven to earth will answer:
   At last the Saviour, Saviour of the world, is King.

William Young Fullerton

33 - A Melody in My Heart

SIDNEY E. COX

1. In my heart there's a glad-some mel-o-dy, A song of cheer is ring-ing clear, For my heav-y bur-den rolled a-way, What a hap-py, hap-py day! _____ In my heart (my heart) to-day, (to-day) There's a mel-o-dy in my heart to-

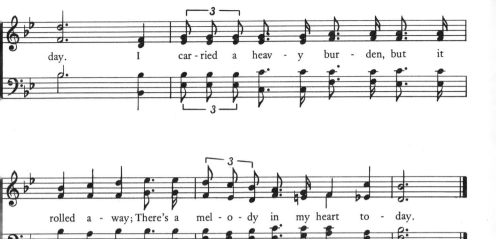

day.   I   car - ried   a   heav - y   bur - den, but   it

rolled   a - way; There's a   mel - o - dy   in   my heart   to - day.

2. It was love wrought the change so wonderful,
    His love for me, beyond degree,
    Found me in the dreary wilderness,
    Filled my heart with happiness.

3. And the way grows brighter ev'ry day,
    What peace is mine! What joy divine!
    And the load of sin that burdened me,
    Rolled away at Calvary.

Sidney E. Cox

34 - He Lives

A. H. ACKLEY

Allegro ♩.= 72

mf

1. I serve a ris - en Sa - viour, He's in the world to - day;____ I
know that He is liv - ing, what - ev - er men may say;____ I
see His hand of mer - cy, I hear His voice of cheer,____ And
just the time I need Him ____ He's al - ways near. ____

CHORUS

He lives, ____ He lives, ____ Christ Je - sus lives ____ to -
He lives, He lives,

day! ___ He walks with me and talks with me a-
long life's nar - row way. ___ He lives, ___ He
lives, ___ He lives, sal - va - tion to im - part! ___ You
ask me how I know He lives? He lives with-in my heart. ___

2. In all the world around me
   I see His loving care;
   And though my heart grows weary,
   I never will despair;
   I know that He is leading
   Through all the stormy blast,
   The day of His appearing
   Will come at last!

3. Rejoice, rejoice, O Christian,
   Lift up your voice and sing
   Eternal hallelujahs
   To Jesus Christ the King;
   The hope of all who seek Him,
   The help of all who find,
   None other is so loving,
   So good and kind.

A. H. Ackley

35 - A Sure Hiding Place

SIDNEY E. COX

Allegro moderato ♩=92

mf

1. In the love of Je - sus I have found a ref - uge,

Though the winds may blow, this one thing I know, He who ne - ver fail - eth is my

cresc.

Shield and Shel - ter, And He leads me where still wa - ters

f

dim.

flow, ____ He leads me where still wa - ters flow. ____

CHORUS

f

Oh, what a hid - ing place, What a pre - cious hid - ing place,

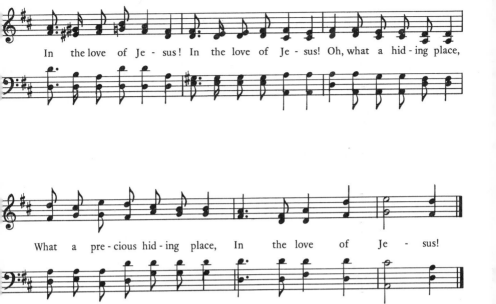

In the love of Je - sus! In the love of Je - sus! Oh, what a hid - ing place,

What a pre - cious hid - ing place, In the love of Je - sus!

2. In His love abiding, in the Rock I'm hiding,
   Lord of life is He, yet He thinks of me;
   Oft-times weak and wayward, yet in great compassion
   Jesus watches, oh, so tenderly,
   He watches, oh, so tenderly.

3. How my soul rejoices in this mighty Saviour,
   His unmeasured grace for a fallen race;
   There upon the cross He wrought so great salvation,
   There, in love divine, He took my place,
   In love divine He took my place.

Sidney E. Cox

36 - God's Love is Wonderful

IRA D. SANKEY

1. God's love to me is won-der-ful, That He should deign to hear ____ The faint-est whis-per of my heart, Wipe from mine eyes the tear; ____ And though I can-not com-pre-hend Such love, so great, so deep, ____ In His strong hands my soul I trust, He will not fail to

CHORUS

keep. _____ God's _____ love is won - der - ful,

God's love is won - der - ful, Won - der - ful __ that

He should give His Son __ to die for me. _____

2. God's love to me is wonderful!
   My very steps are planned;
   When mists of doubt encompass me,
   I hold my Father's hand.
   His love has banished every fear,
   In freedom I rejoice,
   And with my quickened ears I hear
   The music of His voice.

3. God's love to me is wonderful!
   He lights the darkest way;
   I now enjoy His fellowship,
   'Twill last through endless day.
   My Father doth not ask that I
   Great gifts on Him bestow,
   But only that I love Him too,
   And serve Him here below.
                    Sidney E. Cox

37 - He Remembers Sin no More

WILFRED KITCHING

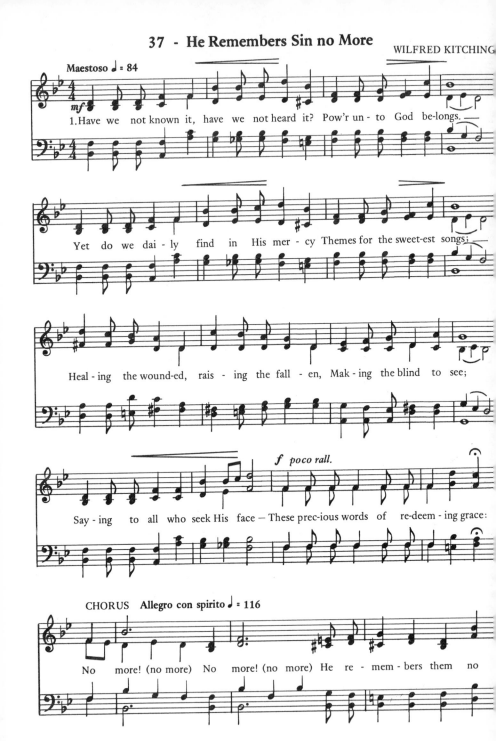

Maestoso ♩ = 84

mf

1.Have we not known it, have we not heard it? Pow'r un-to God be-longs. —

Yet do we dai-ly find in His mer-cy Themes for the sweet-est songs;

Heal-ing the wound-ed, rais-ing the fall-en, Mak-ing the blind to see;

ff poco rall.

Say-ing to all who seek His face — These prec-ious words of re-deem-ing grace:

CHORUS Allegro con spirito ♩ = 116

No more! (no more) No more! (no more) He re-mem-bers them no

2. Joy-bursts of singing gaily are springing
    With ev'ry day that starts.
   If we were silent then would the stones cry
    Shame on our fainting hearts.
   Oh, banish sadness, sing now for gladness!
    Glory in Christ, the Lord!
   "Who is a God like unto Thee,
    One who can pardon iniquity?"

3. Safe in the dark day! safe in the bright day!
    Safe till my latest breath;
   There is endurance in this assurance,
    Stronger than fear of death.
   When the accuser comes to the judgement,
    Seeking my soul to claim,
   I have a token in the Blood,
    I have the word of a pard'ning God.

Albert Orsborn

38 - Heaven Came Down and Glory filled My Soul

Allegretto ♩. = 72

JOHN W. PETERSO

1.Oh, what a won - der - ful, won - der - ful day,

Day I will ne - ver for - get: Af - ter I'd wan - dered in

dark - ness a - way, Je - sus my Sa - viour I met.

Oh, what a ten - der com - pas - sion - ate friend,

He met the need of my heart; Sha - dows dis - pel - ling, With

joy I am tel - ling, He made all the dark - ness de - part.

CHORUS

Hea - ven came down and glo - ry filled my soul, _____

and glo - ry filled my soul,

When at the Cross the Sa-viour made me whole; _____ My

my Sa-viour made me whole; My

sins were washed a - way, _____ And my night was turned to - day, _____

sins were washed a-way,

Hea - ven came down and glo - ry filled my soul. _____

and glo - ry filled my soul.

2. Born of the Spirit with life from above
   Into God's fam'ly divine,
Justified fully through Calvary's love,
   Oh, what a standing is mine!
And the transaction so quickly was made
   When as a sinner I came,
Took of the offer of grace He did proffer,
   He saved me, Oh, praise His dear name!

3. Now I've a hope that will surely endure
   After the passing of time,
I have a future in Heaven for sure,
   There in those mansions sublime.
And it's because of that wonderful day,
   When at the Cross I believed;
Riches eternal and blessings supernal
   From His precious hand I received.

John W. Peterson

39 - I Believe

ARNOLD BROWN

Allegreto ♩ = 112

f

1. On God's word re - ly - ing, Ev - 'ry doubt de - fy - ing,

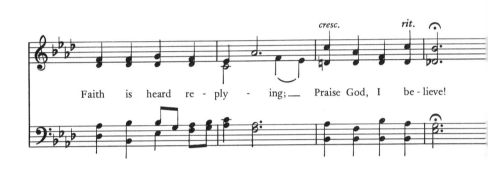

cresc. *rit.*

Faith is heard re - ply - ing; __ Praise God, I be - lieve!

CHORUS *a tempo*

I be - lieve in God the Fa - ther, I be - lieve in God the

Son; I be - lieve in the Ho - ly Spi - rit, Bless - ed

God - head, Three in One; I be - lieve in a full sal - va - tion, In re - demp - tion through the Blood; I be - lieve I'll re - ceive a crown of life, When I hear the Lord's "Well done".

2. Confidence unshaken;
   When bereft, forsaken,
   E'en if life be taken,
      Praise God, I believe!

3. Peace and joy unending
   In my soul are blending,
   Faith on love depending,
      Praise God, I believe!

Arnold Brown

40 - I Know Whom I Have Believed

Allegro ♩ = 112

JAMES McGRANAHAN

I know not why God's won-drous grace To me He hath made known; Nor

why, un-wor-thy of such grace, He claimed me for His own.

CHORUS

But "I know whom I have be-liev-ed, and am per-suad-ed that He is

a-ble To keep that which I've com-mit-ted Un-to Him a-gainst that day.

2. I know not how this saving faith
    To me He did impart,
Nor how believing in His Word
    Wrought peace within my heart.

3. I know not how the Spirit moves,
    Convincing men of sin;
Revealing Jesus through the Word,
    Creating faith in Him.

4. I know not what of good or ill
    May be reserved for me,
Of weary ways or golden days,
    Before His face I see.

5. I know not when my Lord may come,
    At night or noon - day fair;
Nor if I'll walk the vale with Him,
    Or meet Him in the air.

Daniel W. Whittle

41 - He Lifted Me

Andante ♩ = 72

CHARLES H. GABRIEL

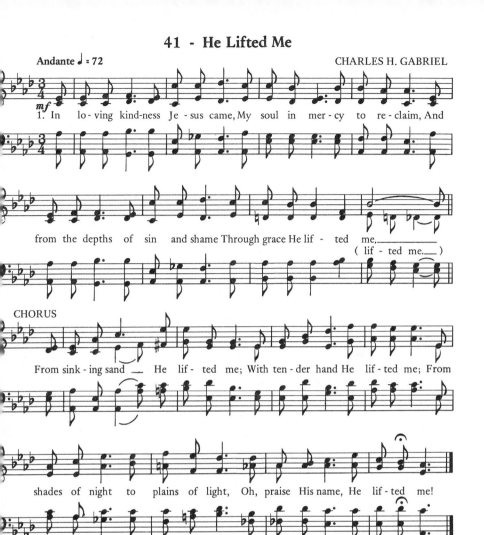

1. In lo - ving kind-ness Je - sus came, My soul in mer - cy to re - claim, And from the depths of sin and shame Through grace He lif - ted me.
(lif - ted me.)

CHORUS

From sink - ing sand He lif - ted me; With ten - der hand He lif - ted me; From shades of night to plains of light, Oh, praise His name, He lif - ted me!

2. He called me long before I heard,
Before my sinful heart was stirred;
But when I took Him at His word,
Forgiven, He lifted me.

3. His brow was pierced by many a thorn,
His hands by cruel nails were torn,
When from my guilt and grief, forlorn,
In love, He lifted me.

4. Now on a higher plane I dwell,
And with my soul I know 'tis well;
Yet how or why, I cannot tell,
He should have lifted me.

Charlotte G. Homer

42 - Love Lifted Me

HOWARD E. SMITH

Allegretto ♩.= 72

1. I was sink - ing deep in sin, Far from the peace - ful shore; ____
Ve - ry deep - ly stained with - in, Sink - ing to rise no more; ____
But the Mas - ter of the sea, Heard my des - pair - ing cry, ____
From the wa - ters lift - ed me, Now safe am I. ____

CHORUS

Love lift - ed me, ____ Love lift - ed me. ____
(lift - ed me) (lift - ed me)

When ___ no - one but Christ could help, ___ love lift - ed me. ___

Love lift - ed me, _____ Love lift - ed me, _____
(lift - ed me) (lift - ed me)

When ___ no - one but Christ could help, ___ Love lift - ed me.

2. All my heart to Him I give,
   Ever to Him I'll cling;
   In His blessed presence live,
   Ever His praises sing.
   Love so mighty and so true
   Merits my soul's best songs,
   Faithful, loving service, too,
   To Him belongs.

3. Souls in danger, look above,
   Jesus completely saves;
   He will lift you by His love
   Out of the angry waves.
   He's the Master of the sea,
   Billows His will obey,
   He your Saviour wants to be —
   Be saved today.

James Rowe

43 - My Saviour's Love

Moderato ♩ = 96

CHARLES H. GABRIEL

mf

1. I stand a-mazed in the pres-ence Of Je-sus the Naz-a-rene, And

won-der how He could love me, A sin-ner, con-demned, un-clean.

f CHORUS

How mar-vel-ous! how won-der-ful! And my song shall ev-er be:
(A.T.B.) Oh, how mar-vel-ous! oh, how won-der-ful!

How mar-vel-ous! how won-der-ful Is my Sav-iour's love for me!
Oh, how mar-vel-ous! oh, how won-der-ful

2. For me it was in the garden
   He prayed, "Not my will, but Thine";
   He had no tears for His own griefs,
   But sweat drops of blood for mine.

3. He took my sins and my sorrows,
   He made them His very own;
   He bore my burden to Calvary,
   And suffered and died alone.

4. When with the ransomed in glory
   His face I at last shall see,
   'Twill be my joy through the ages
   To sing of His love for me.

Charles H. Gabriel

44 - I Walk with the King

B. D. ACKLEY

Allegretto ♩. = 54

mf

1. In sor-row I wan-dered, my spi-rit op-pressed, But now I am hap-py se-

cure-ly I rest; From morn-ing till even-ing glad ca-rols I sing, And

cresc. *rall.* CHORUS Piu mosso ♩. = 66

f

this is the rea-son, I walk with the King. I walk with the King, Hal-le-

f

lu-jah!__ I walk with the King, praise His name!__ No long-er I roam, my

soul fa-ces home, I walk and I talk with the King._____

2. For years in the fetters of sin I was bound,
   The world could not help me — no comfort I found;
   But now, like the birds and the sunbeams of spring,
   I'm free and rejoicing,— I walk with the King!

3. O soul near despair in the lowlands of strife,
   Look up and let Jesus come into your life;
   The joy of salvation to you He would bring,
   Come into the sunlight and walk with the King!

James Rowe

45 - Now I Belong to Jesus

2. Once I was lost in sin's degredation,
   Jesus came down to bring me salvation;
   Lifted me up from sorrow and shame,
   Now I belong to Him.

3. Joy floods my soul for Jesus has saved me,
   Freed me from sin that long had enslaved me,
   His precious blood He gave to redeem,
   Now I belong to Him.

Norman J. Clayton

46 - When His Love Reached Me

Moderato ♩ = 100

SIDNEY E. COX

1. It was love reached me when— far a - way, The love of my prec - ious
Sa - viour; He gave Him - self my debt to pay, My won - der - ful, won - der - ful
Sa - viour.

CHORUS f

When His love reached me He set my heart a - sing - ing, When His
love reached me, won-drous love reached me; And the bells of Heav'n with
rall.
har-mo-ny are ring - ing, For His love (won-drous love) reached me (His love reached me).

2. It is love that keeps me day by day,
   The love of my precious Saviour;
   He guides me lest my feet should stray,
   My wonderful, wonderful Saviour.

3. It is love supplies my ev'ry need,
   The love of my precious Saviour;
   The Bread of life my soul to feed,
   My wonderful, wonderful Saviour.

Sidney E. Cox

47 - Singing "Ebenezer"

Allegro moderato ♩ = 96

EDWARD J.

mf

1. Lord of my life and God of my Sal - va - tion,

No - thing am I want - ing with Him by my side; ___

In pas - tures green, by qui - et ways He lead - eth,

In the paths of peace my ran - som'd soul doth guide.

CHORUS

f

All thro' the years ___ His pro - vi - dence has led me,

His a-bound-ing good-ness has been all my song; ____
All thro' the years I tell His love and mer - cy,
Sing - ing "E - be - ne - zer" as the years roll on.

2. Yea, though I tread the valley of the shadow,
Nothing will I fear for He the path doth know;
His rod and staff shall be my safe supporting,
Comforting and guiding every step I go.

3. When fierce temptations round about me gather,
When the foe is near to harass and alarm,
Calm is my heart and happy is my resting,
Surely I shall dwell in peace for evermore.

Edward Joy

48 - The Song in my Heart

SIDNEY E. COX

Allegro moderato ♩ = 116

1. There's a song that's ring-ing in my heart to-day, For I've

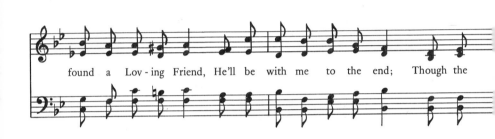

found a Lov-ing Friend, He'll be with me to the end; Though the

temp-ter's snares be-set my path be-low, He is ev-er by my

side I know. In my heart a song is ring-ing, _____ For He

par - doned me I know just be - cause He loved me so. And I'm

sing - ing, sing - ing, sing - ing _____ Just be - cause He loved me so.

2. There's a song that's ringing in my heart today,
   Jesus' power has set me free,
   And He gives me victory;
   All my sin stains vanished in the crimson flow,
   And He'll keep me ev'ry hour I know.

3. There's a song that's ringing in my heart today,
   For I'll see my Saviour's face
   At the ending of the race;
   Wear a spotless robe as white as driven snow,
   Hear the welcome from the King I know.

Sidney E. Cox

49 - This is What the Lord has Done

SIDNEY COX

1. I want to tell what God has done, Through Christ, His well be-lo-vèd Son, How my poor heart He sought and won; Can you won-der that I want to tell__ it? I want to tell what God can do For sin-ners lost like me and you, Of sins washed white and gar-ments new; Can you won-der that I want to tell it?

CHORUS

I want to tell you what the Lord has done, What the Lord has done for me (for me): H

lift - ed me from the mi - ry clay; Oh, what a hap-py day! ___

I want to tell you what the Lord can do, What the Lord can do for

you (for you): He can take your life as He did mine, And make it a-new.

2. I want to tell of saving grace,
   Of God's strong arm, His warm embrace,
Of Blood that can all sins erase;
   Can you wonder that I want to tell it?
I want to tell to sinners lost
   That Christ has paid sin's fearful cost,
And saves unto the uttermost;
   Can you wonder that I want to tell it?

3. What God has done, He still can do;
   His pow'r can fashion lives anew,
And all who trust Him find Him true;
   Can you wonder that I want to tell it?
I want to tell of that glad day
   For which we watch, for which we pray,
It must be near, not far away;
   Can you wonder that I want to tell it?

Sidney Cox

50 - We Have a Gospel

JOHN GOWANS

JOHN LARSSON

Allegro ♩ = 88

We have a gos-pel that match-es the hour,
Man is a weak-ling but he can be strong,

[1]
We have dis-covered the true source of power,
Choos-ing the

[2]
right and re-fus-ing the wrong. Man has no

mean-ing, no pur-pose, no soul, Till he dis-

51 - The Old, Old Story is True

E. O. EXCELL

Allegretto ♩.= 62

mf

1. There's a won-der-ful sto-ry I heard long a-go, ___ 'Tis called, "The sweet sto-ry of old"; ___ I hear it so of-ten, When-ev-er I go, ___ That same ___ old sto-ry is told; ___ And I thought it was strange that so oft-en they tell That sto-ry as if it were new, ___ But I've found out the rea-son they

cresc.

2. They told of a Saviour so loving and pure,
   Who came down among men to dwell,
   To seek for His lost ones and make them secure
   From death and the power of hell;
   He was spurned and despised, and with thorns He was crowned,
   On a cross was extended to view;
   But what joy and sweet peace in my heart when I found
   That old, old story is true.

   D. B. Watkins

52 - A Prayer

Andante ♩ = 72   JOHN LARSSON

1. Kneel - ing in pen - i - tence I make my prayer,
Own - ing my weak - ness - es and my des - pair;
Fail - ure I can - not hide, brok - en my self - ish pride,
Par - don Thou dost pro - vide, Par - don de - clare.

2. Nothing can I achieve, nothing attain,
   He that without Thee builds, labours in vain;
   Shatter my own design,
   Shaping a plan Divine,
   Come to this heart of mine
       Saviour, again.

3. Though few the gifts I have that Thou canst use,
   Make Thy demands on me, I'll not refuse;
   Take all there is of me,
   Take what I hope to be,
   Thy way at last I see,
       Thy way I choose.

John Gowans

53 - Channels Only

ADA ROSE GIBBS

Moderato ♩ = 76

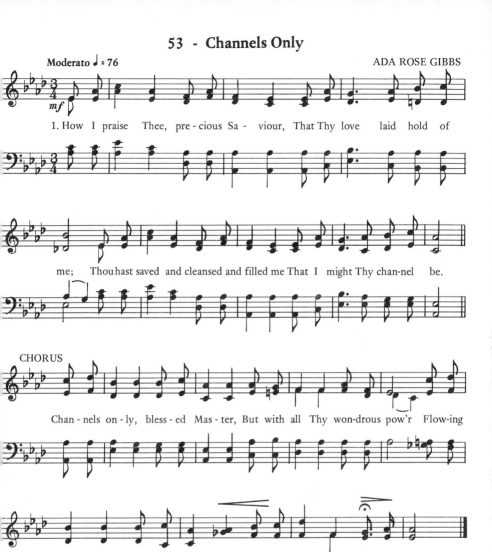

1. How I praise Thee, pre-cious Sa-viour, That Thy love laid hold of me; Thou hast saved and cleansed and filled me That I might Thy chan-nel be.

CHORUS

Chan-nels on-ly, bless-ed Mas-ter, But with all Thy won-drous pow'r Flow-ing thro' me, Thou canst use me, Ev-'ry day and ev-'ry hour.

2. Emptied, that Thou shouldest fill me,
A clean vessel in Thy hand;
With no power but as Thou givest
Graciously with each command.

3. Witnessing Thy power to save me,
Setting free from self and sin;
Thou who boughtest to possess me,
In Thy fulness, Lord, come in.

4. Jesus, fill now with Thy Spirit
Hearts that full surrender know;
That the streams of living water
From our inner man may flow.

Mary E. Maxwell

54 - All My Days and All My Hours

Andante moderato ♩ = 76

EDWARD H. JOY

1. Thou did'st give Thy-self to me On the

cross, where Thou did'st die; I would give my-self to

cresc.

Thee While the days are go - ing by. Where the

dim.

p cresc.

King, my Lord, may be, There for ev - er would I stay; In the

mf

cen - tre of Thy will I would be, for now and aye.

dim.

CHORUS

pp　　　　　　　　　　　　　　　　　　　　　　　　*cresc. poco a poco*

All　my　days,　and　all　my　hours;　All　my　will,　and　all　my

powers;　All　the　pas - sion　of　my　soul,　Not　a　frag - ment,　but　the

f　　　　　　　　　　　　　　*dim.*

whole　　Shall　be　Thine,　dear　Lord,　Shall　be　Thine,　dear　Lord.

2. Let the worldlings pass Thee by,
　　Nothing lovely in Thee see;
　As a root in dreary ground
　　To the many Thou may'st be:
　Yet the passion of my soul
　　Goeth out to call Thee mine;
　All the passion of Thy soul
　　Goeth out to call me Thine.

3. Still the days are passing by,
　　End of time is coming on;
　Days of service less and less,
　　Chances soon will all be gone.
　Help me use the days that are,
　　Help me give my little all;
　Labour on till Thou dost give
　　That last loving, homeward call.

Edward H. Joy

55 - All There is of Me, Lord

Allegro moderato ♩ = 96

SIDNEY E. COX

1. All there is of me,—— Lord, At Thy feet I lay,——

Now Thy gra - cious pur - pose, Oh, ful-fil, I pray! Each

mo - ment, Lord, be spent for Thee, Thou shalt have all there is of me.

mf
CHORUS

All there is of me, Lord, All there is of me,

Time and ta - lents, day by day, All I bring to Thee:——

All there is of me, Lord, All there is of me,
On Thine al - tar here I lay, ___ All there is of me.

2. All there is of me, Lord,
      Time and talents Thine,
   Mould me as Thou wilt, Lord,
      Make my life to shine
   So men may find a way to Thee;
      Use all, yes, all there is of me.

3. All there is of me, Lord,
      Gladly now I bring,
   Let the fire from heaven
      Seal the offering;
   For time and for eternity
      Take all, yes, all there is of me.

Sidney E. Cox

56 - At Peace with my God

Moderato ♩.= 63

EDWARD JOY

mp

1. At peace with my God;_____ Oh, bliss be - yond mea - sure_____

_____ That I should ob - tain_____ This won - der - ful

cresc.

trea - sure:_____ Be a - ble to sing_____ In sor - row or

dim.

plea - sure_____ That I am at peace,_____ At peace with my God._____

CHORUS

At peace with my God (with my God): But how can it

be (how can it be), Ex-cept by the love (by the

love) of Je-sus for me? _____ An-xi-e-ty

(TEN.) of Je-sus for me?

gone: _____ Sins un-der the Blood: _____

An-xi-e-ty gone: (TEN.) Sins un-der the

And I am at peace (at peace), At peace with my God. _____

Blood:

2. Anxiety gone; oh, bliss beyond measure
   That I should obtain this wonderful treasure;
   Be able to sing in sorrow or pleasure
   That I am at peace, at peace with my God.

3. At peace with my God; indwelt by the Spirit;
   Redeemed by the Blood, though born without merit.
   God's judgement will come, but I will not fear it,
   For I am at peace, at peace with my God.

4. At peace with my God; though fainting and failing;
   Sin's temptations and trials my weakness assailing:
   But God is near by in power prevailing,
   And I am at peace, at peace with my God.

Verses 1 & 2 Edward Joy   Verses 3 & 4 Ernest Miller

57 - In the Love of Jesus

(Gb)

Moderato ♩ = 88

WILLIAM HAMMOND

Like to a lamb who from the fold has strayed

Far on the moun-tain, of the dark a - fraid,

Seek - ing a shel - ter from the night's a - larm,

Long-ing for com-fort of the shep-herds arm. So Je - sus found me

cresc.   *dim.*

on sin's moun-tain drear, __ Gath-ered me close and ban-ished all my fear.

CHORUS più mosso ♩ = 110

In the love of Je-sus there is all I need, While I fol-low close-ly where my Lord may lead; By His grace for-giv-en, (Ten. and Bass) By His grace for - giv-en, In His pre-sence blest, In the love of Je-sus, In the love of Je-sus, is per - fect rest.

2. Like to a pilgrim in an unknown land
   Seeking the comfort of a guiding hand,
   Fearing the perils of the winding way,
   Pleading for strength sufficient every day,
   I met my Lord! And though the path be dim
   He knows the way and I will walk with Him.

3. Like to a child who, when the night may fall,
   Out of the darkness hears his father call,
   Far and a-weary though his feet may roam
   Sees in the distant shining lights of home,
   So at the last the music of His voice
   Will calm my fears and make my heart rejoice.

Ivy Mawby

(G♭)

58 - The Greatest of These

Andante con espress. ♩ = 69

GEORGE MARSHA[

1. Though in de-clar-ing Christ to the sin-ner, I may all men su[

pass, ___ If love im-pas-sioned seal not the mes-sage, I am nought bu[

CHORUS

sound-ing brass. Love suf-f'reth pa-tient-ly; Love work-eth si-lent-ly;

Love seek-eth not her own. Love ne-ver fail-eth; ___

Love still pre-vail-eth. Lord, in me Thy love ___ en-throne!

2. Though I have wisdom lighting all myst'ries;
   Though I may all things know;
   Though great my faith be, removing mountains —
   Without love 'tis empty show.

3. Though I distribute all my possessions;
   Though as a martyr die;
   My sacrifices profit me nothing,
   Unless love doth sanctify.

Arch. R. Wiggins

59 - Follow thou Me

Andante con espress. ♪ = 72

SIDNEY E. COX

1. By the peace-ful shores of Gal - i - lee, Mend-ing their nets by the silv - 'ry sea, The fish - er - men toiled at their tasks each day, Till the Mas - ter walk - eth a - long that way.

CHORUS a tempo

"Fol - low thou Me", He calls a - gain, "And I will make you fish - ers of men". As in the days by Gal - i - lee, Je - sus is call - ing you and me.

2. And they left their nets when they heard His voice,
Making the Master's call their choice,
And they toiled with Him for the world astray,
To bring men back to the Father's way.

3. And the self-same voice is heard today,
Calling men in the self-same way
As the fishermen heard by Galilee,
"Leave now your nets and follow Me".

Sidney E. Cox

60 - Higher Ground

CHARLES H. GABRIEL

Moderato ♩ = 72

1. I'm press-ing on the up-ward way, New heights I'm gain - ing ev - 'ry day; Still pray-ing as I on-ward bound, Lord, plant my feet on high - er ground.

CHORUS

Lord, lift me up and let me stand, By faith, on Heav - en's ta - ble - land; A high - er plane than I have found; Lord, plant my feet on high - er ground.

2. My heart has no desire to stay
   Where doubts arise and fears dismay;
   While some may dwell where these abound,
   My prayer, my aim, is higher ground.

3. I want to live above the world
   Though Satan's darts at me are hurled;
   For faith has caught the joyful sound,
   The song of saints on higher ground.

4. I want to scale the utmost height
   And catch a gleam of glory bright,
   But still I pray, till Heaven I've found,
   Lord, lead me on to higher ground.

Johnson Oatman

61 - I am Praying

WILLIAM J. KIRKPATRICK

Andante con espress. ♩ = 72

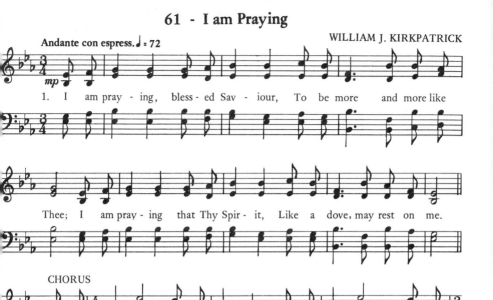

1. I am pray - ing, bless - ed Sav - iour, To be more and more like

Thee; I am pray - ing that Thy Spir - it, Like a dove, may rest on me.

CHORUS

Thou who know - est all my weak - ness, Thou who know-est all my

dim.

care, While I plead each pre - cious pro-mise, Hear, O hear, and an - swer prayer.

2. I am praying, blessed Saviour,
　　For a faith so clear and bright
　That its eye may see Thy glory
　　Through the deepest, darkest night.

3. I am praying to be humbled
　　By the power of grace divine,
　To be clothed upon with meekness
　　And to have no will but Thine.

4. I am praying, blessed Saviour,
　　And my constant prayer shall be
　For a perfect consecration
　　That shall make me more like Thee.

Fanny Crosby

62 - Lord, Make Calvary Real to Me

SIDNEY E. COX

Allegretto ♩ = 116

1. Though cen - tu - ries ___ have fled a - way ___ Since that dark morn - ing, cold ___ and grey, When, up the way of thorn and stone, Thy gen - tle feet did tread ___ a - lone; Wilt Thou, O Lord, make real to me The ma - jes - ty ___ of Cal - va - ry

CHORUS

Lord, make Cal - va - ry real to me,

Lord, make Cal - va - ry real to me; _____

cresc.

Op - en mine eyes to see vic - t'ry in Christ for me,

dim.

Lord, make Cal - va - ry real _____ to me.

2. Here is the place of heav'nly grace,
   For ev'ry child of Adam's race;
   Thou didst my sin upon Thee bear,
   And free my soul from Satan's snare;
   In confidence I claim from Thee
   The liberty of Calvary.

3. Sin shall no more dominion have,
   Gone are the shackles of the slave;
   No condemnation now remains,
   For Calvary the vict'ry gains;
   Dead unto sin, alive in Thee,
   Thou conquering One of Calvary.

Sidney E. Cox

63 - My Jesus, I Love Thee

Andante ♩=72

Tune: Flow gently sweet Aftc

mp

1. My Je - sus, I love Thee, I know Thou art mine, For Thee all the

pleas-ures of sin I re - sign; My grac-ious Re - deem-er, my Sav - iour art

mf

Thou, If ev - er I loved Thee, my Je - sus, 'tis now. I

love Thee be - cause Thou hast first lov - èd me, And pur - chased my

cresc.   *rit.*   *f*   *a tempo*

par - don on Cal - va - ry's tree; I love Thee for wear - ing the

thorns on Thy brow, If ev - er I loved Thee, my Je - sus, 'tis now.

2. I will love Thee in life, I will love Thee in death,
And praise Thee as long as Thou lendest me breath;
And say, when the death-dew lies cold on my brow:
If ever I loved Thee, my Jesus, 'tis now.
I love Thee because Thou hast first lovèd me,
And purchased my pardon on Calvary's tree;
I love Thee for wearing the thorns on Thy brow,
If ever I loved Thee, My Jesus, 'tis now.

3. In mansions of glory and endless delight,
I'll ever adore Thee and dwell in Thy sight;
I'll sing with the glittering crown on my brow:
If ever I loved Thee, my Jesus, 'tis now.
I love Thee because Thou has first lovèd me,
And purchased my pardon on Calvary's tree;
I love Thee for wearing the thorns on Thy brow,
If ever I loved Thee, my Jesus, 'tis now.

Ralph Featherstone

64 - I Would be like Jesus

Moderato ♩. = 72

BENTLEY D. ACKLEY

1. Earth-ly pleas-ures vain-ly call me, I would be like Je - sus;

Noth-ing world-ly shall en-thrall me, I would be like Je - sus.

CHORUS

Be like Je-sus, this my song, In the home and in the throng;

Be like Je-sus, all day long! I would be like Je - sus.

2. He has broken every fetter,
   I would be like Jesus;
   That my soul may serve Him better,
   I would be like Jesus.

3. All the way from earth to glory,
   I would be like Jesus;
   Telling o'er and o'er the story,
   I would be like Jesus.

4. That in Heaven He may meet me,
   I would be like Jesus;
   That His words "Well done" may greet me,
   I would be like Jesus.

James Rowe

65 - Out of my Bondage

Andante ♩.= 40 (♩ =120)

GEORGE C. STEBBINS

1. Out of my bond-age, sor-row and night, Je-sus, I come! Je-sus, I come! In-to Thy free-dom, glad-ness and light, Je-sus, I come to Thee (to Thee)! __ Out of my sick-ness in-to Thy health, Out of my want and in-to Thy wealth, __ Out of my sin and in-to Thy-self, Je-sus, I come to Thee! __

2. Out of my shameful failure and loss,
   Jesus, I come! Jesus, I come!
Into the glorious gain of Thy cross,
   Jesus, I come to Thee!
Out of earth's sorrows into Thy balm,
Out of life's storms and into the calm,
Out of distress to jubilant psalm,
   Jesus, I come to Thee!

3. Out of the fear and dread of the tomb,
   Jesus I come! Jesus I come!
Into the joy and light of Thy home,
   Jesus I come to Thee!
Out of the depths of ruin untold,
Into the peace of Thy sheltering fold,
Ever Thy glorious face to behold,
   Jesus, I come to Thee!

W. T. Sleeper

66 - Spirit Divine

BRINDLEY BOON

Andante con molto espress. ♩ = 84

p
1. Spi-rit Di-vine, come as____ of old____ With heal-ing in Thy

mf
train; Come, as Thou did'st, to sanc-ti-fy; Let nought of sin re-main.

CHORUS Allegretto ♩. = 60
p
Come,____ Great Spi - rit, Come;____
Come, Great Spi - rit, Come, oh, come;____

cresc. ... *f*
Make____ each heart Thy Home.____ En-ter ev-
Make each heart Thy Home.____

p rall.
long - ing soul; Come,____ Great Spi - rit, come.____

2. Spirit Divine, purge Thou our hearts,
   Make us to understand
   Thy blessed will concerning us,
   And teach us Love's command.

3. Spirit Divine, cleanse Thou our souls
   With Pentecostal flood;
   Breathe into us the life that shows
   The Father-love of God.

Brindley Boon

67 - Take up thy Cross

Andante con espress. ♩ = 80

A. H. ACKLEY

1. I walked one day a - long a coun - try road, And there a strang - er jour - neyed too; Bent low be - neath the bur - den of His load; It was a cross, a cross I knew.

CHORUS *mf*

"Take up thy cross and fol - low Me", I hear the bless - ed Sa - viour call, How can I make a less - er sac - ri - fice, When Je - sus gave His all?

I cried, "Lord Jesus", and He spoke my name;
I saw His hands all bruis'd and torn;
I stooped to kiss away the marks of shame,
The shame for me that He had borne.

3. "O let me bear Thy cross dear Lord", I cried,
And lo, a cross for me appeared;
The one, forgotten, I had cast aside,
The one so long that I had feared.

A. H. Ackley

68 - Follow On!

ROBERT LOWRY

Moderato ♩ = 116

1 Down in the val - ley with my Sav - iour I would go,

Where the flowers are bloom - ing and the sweet wat - ers flow;

Ev - 'ry - where He leads me I would fol - low, fol - low on,

Walk - ing in His foot - steps till the crown be won.

CHORUS

Fol - low! Fol - low! I will fol - low Jes - sus!

An - y - where, ev - 'ry - where, I will fol - low on!

Fol - low! Fol - low! I will fol - low Jes - sus!

Ev - 'ry - where He leads me I will fol - low on.

2. Down in the valley with my Saviour I would go,
   Where the storms are sweeping and the dark waters flow;
   With His hand to lead me I will never, never fear:
   Dangers cannot fright me if my Lord is near.

3. Down in the valley, or upon the mountain steep,
   Close beside my Saviour would my soul ever keep;
   He will lead me safely in the path that He has trod,
   Up to where they gather on the hills of God.

W. O. Cushing

69 - Touch Me again Lord

Andante con espress. ♩ = 72

W. PAINE

1. Lord, when the crowd ga - thered round Thee for heal - ing, There, midst the num - ber, I put in my claim; Vir - tue from Thee, Lord, was found at that mo - ment, I felt I was whole, and I blessed Thy dear name.

CHORUS

Oh, touch me a - gain, Lord, touch me a - gain! This mo - ment I feel a - fresh Thou canst heal, So touch me a - gain, Lord, Oh touch me a - gain!

2. I have not dwelt in the joy of Thy presence;
   Thou canst the health of my soul now restore,
   Love has grown less, and my faith has been wounded,
   Oh, wonderful Healer, come, heal me once more.

3. Waiting, I feel, Lord, the joy of Thy presence,
   Now is a chance which Thy love doth allow,
   While Thou art passing, O Lord, Thou canst heal me,
   So stretch forth Thy hand, Lord, and touch me just now.

Mrs. H. A. Beavan

70 - Make Me Aware of Thee

Andante ♩ = 72   (St. Catherine)

HENRI F. HEMY

1. Make me a-ware __ of Thee, __ O Lord, As in Thy tem - ple
I __ give praise; At - ten - tive to __ Thy ho - ly word,
Or in glad song my voice __ to raise. That I may feel Thy
Spi - rit's power, Oh, come, in - vade my soul this hour.

2. Make me aware of Thee, O Lord,
   As supplicant, I bow the knee.
   My faith, though small, wilt Thou reward
   That contact I may make with Thee
   And thus obtain that inward calm
   That makes of life a living Psalm.

3. Make me aware of Thee, O Lord,
   As with Thy children I unite
   To share that wondrous heritage
   Of Calvary and Easter light.
   O Master, let Thy people be
   Consistently aware of Thee.

                    Vic. Ottaway

71 - Great and Glorious

Andante con espress. ♩ = 56

ALBERT DALZIEL

1. Je - su', oh, Je - su', all fair art Thou and Ho - ly!

Pure is Thy rai - ment, Thy pre - sence as the light;

cresc. poco a poco

Here we ac - claim Thee, whose spi - rit meek and low - ly,

Calls us to wor - ship, yet shames us in Thy sight.

King of all the earth! Man of low - ly birth!

Je - sus the Son,_____ Suf - fer - ing One! _____

Love has sub - dued us, to Thee our hearts are won.

2. Jesu', oh Jesu', whose blood for us has spoken,
    Pleading our ransom within the Holy Place:
Stay the avenger! Thy dying is our token -
    Save from our Egypt the whole of Adam's race.
Be Thou Lord of us! Guide our exodus
Out of the night, into the light!
We are a people depending on Thy might!

3. Jesu', oh Jesu', to live as in Thy presence!
    Sad with Thy sadness, rejoicing in Thy joys;
Life, love and blessing, of these art Thou the essence,
    Far, far transcending all earthly pomp and noise!
Spread Thy kindly wing for our covering,
In Thy dear side Thy suppliants hide,
Cause us to know Thee, lest earth our love divide.

Albert Orsborn

72 - Just Where He Needs Me

And since He found me, By love He's bound me

rall.

To serve Him joy - ful - ly. (joy - ful - ly.)

What can I do to ease life's heavy burdens?
　What can I do to help mankind in need?
Just where I am I'll share my neighbour's hardship,
　Lighten his load, and prove a friend indeed.

3. What can I do to justify my living?
　What can I be to make this life worth while?
I'll be a voice to call men to the Saviour,
　Just where I am, and win my Father's smile.

Miriam Richards

73 - Amazing Grace

Andante ♩ = 72

Early American Melody

mf

1. A-maz - ing grace! how sweet the sound, That saved a wretch like me! I

once___ was lost, but now___ am found, Was blind, but now I see.

'Twas grace that taught my heart to fear,
　And grace my fears relieved;
How precious did that grace appear
　The hour I first believed!

3. Through many dangers, toils and snares
　I have already come;
Tis grace has brought me safe thus far,
　And grace will lead me home.

The Lord has promised good to me,
　His word my hope secures;
He will my shield and portion be
　As long as life endures.

5. And when this flesh and heart shall fail
　And mortal life shall cease;
I shall possess within the veil
　A life of joy and peace.

6. When we've been there ten thousand years,
　Bright shining as the sun,
We've no less days to sing God's praise
　Than when we first begun.

John Newton

74 - A Hymn of Faith

JOHN B. DYKE
Tune: Alfor

1. E - ter - nal God, un - chan - ging Through all the chan - ging years, Whos hand all things cre - a - ted, Who holds the count-less stars; En throned in heaven - ly glo - ry, Yet not a God a - far: Thou deign - est to have dwel - ling Here where Thy peo - ple are.

2. Forbid that man's achievements
   Should cause our faith to wane,
   Or seek in human wisdom
   Our spirit to sustain;
   Lord, surely Thou art shaping
   All things to Thy design,
   And born of this conviction
   Is faith to match our time.

3. And in a world divided
   By selfishness and guile,
   When Truth is on the scaffold
   And Faith is standing trial,
   Grant us, by inward knowledge
   No learning can bestow,
   A faith that answers firmly —
   "These things, these things I know".

4. Though men have wrought confusion
   Thy hand still holds the plan,
   And Thou, at length, decideth
   The destiny of man;
   Dominions rise and perish,
   The mighty have their day,
   But still Thy Word abideth,
   It shall not pass away.

Albert Dalziel

(Gb)

75 - The Pathway of Duty

Allegro moderato ♩ = 112

SIDNEY E. COX

mf

1. There's a path that's some-times thorn-y, There's a nar-row way, and straight; It is

called the path of du-ty, And it leads to Hea-ven's gate. While we
Hea-ven's gate.

mp

tread this path of du-ty, We will find our needs sup-plied From the ri-ver of God's

mf CHORUS

mer-cy That is flow-ing close be-side. By the path-way of du-ty Flows the

ri-ver of God's grace: By the path-way of du-ty Flows the ri-ver of God's grace.

2. 'Tis a blessed way and holy,
   'Tis a path of peace and joy;
   Though sometimes the way be stony,
   And the cares of life annoy.
   But this path that we call duty,
   Is the way the Master trod,
   And the smile of love and beauty
   Lights the way that leads to God.

3. Let us walk this path of duty
   With our faces to the sun;
   Carry all our burdens gladly,
   Finish well what we've begun.
   From the river of God's mercy
   That is flowing by the way,
   We may drink and find refreshing
   For the burdens of the day.

Sidney E. Cox

76 - A Never-failing Friend

(Gb) Andante moderato ♩ = 108

HERBERT BOOTH

1. A Friend I have found who my needs hath sup - plied, A Friend who my

sor - rows hath soothed, _____ A Friend who no bless - ing my

soul hath de - nied, Nor suf - fered my heart to be moved. _____ He

smiles! I am blest; He rules! I have rest; His Pre - sence de -

stroys ev - 'ry fear; _____ How can I be ev - er by

sor - row op - pressed, With Je - sus my spi - rit to cheer!

CHORUS *f* **Allegretto ♩. = 60**

A ne - ver - fail - ing Friend, A ne - ver - fail - ing Friend Is

Christ to me, so rich and free, His fa - vours ne - ver end. A

ne - ver - fail - ing Friend, A ne - ver - fail - ing Friend Give

up your sin, and you shall win This ne - ver - fail - ing Friend.

This friend I have found, no respecter is He,
    All classes with Him are the same;
The poor and the rich, and the bond and the free
    His mercy and pardon may claim.
I sought, He was near; I prayed, He did hear;
    I proved that He loved even me;
I rose from the tomb of sorrow and fear,
    And claimed Him my Saviour to be.

3. A Friend I have found who has taught me the charm
    Of loving the purest and best,
And into the wounds of my heart poured the balm
    Of healing and comfort and rest;
His pain brings renown, His Cross brings the crown,
    To serve Him is now my one care;
And here at the Cross I have laid myself down,
    And trust to be kept ever there.

Herbert Booth

77 - A Perfect Trust

Andantino M. ♪ = 96

CORNELIE BOOTH

1. When I pon-der o'er the sto-ry Of my life's de-
feat and grief, How much mis-er-y and blind-ness
I can trace to un-be-lief! Oh, how man-y
fights I've lost, All for want of faith to trust!

CHORUS Lento con espress. M. ♩ = 48

Oh, for a deep-er, Oh, for a great-er,

Oh, for a per - fect ___ trust in the Lord!

Oh, for a deep - er, Oh, for a great - er,

Oh, for a per - fect ___ trust in the Lord!

2. Can I wonder I have faltered?
　　 Can I be surprised to fall?
　When my faith could most have saved me,
　　 I have trusted least of all.
　When my own resources fail,
　　 Then His power should most prevail.

3. If to grace there is no limit,
　　 Why should I be slow to plead?
　If thy power is not restricted,
　　 Why not speak my ev'ry need?
　All the treasures of His throne,
　　 Faith will make them all my own.

4. Yes, dear Saviour, I will trust Thee,
　　 Live by faith and not by sight;
　Knowing Thou art close beside me,
　　 Giving vic'try in the fight.
　Jesus, while Thou art so near,
　　 I will never, never fear.

Cornelie Booth

78 - Casting All Your Care on Him

Moderato ♩ = 92

SIDNEY R. HUBBARD

1. There is strength in know-ing Je - sus, When your heart is bowed with care (bowed with care); 'Mid the pro-blems that dis-tress you, Oh, what joy to feel Him there (feel Him there).

mf CHORUS

Cast - ing all your care on Him, Cast - ing all your care on Him, In His prom-is-es con-fid-ing, In His might-y love a-bid-ing, Cast - ing all your care on Him (your care on Him).

Cast - ing your care on Him, (on Him), Cast - ing your care on Him (on Him),

2. When the darkness round you gathers,
   When your path seems hid from sight,
   Jesus then in love is watching,
   And He always leads aright.

3. There is peace which passes knowledge,
   And a joy no tongue can tell,
   When we bring our cares to Jesus,
   Hear Him whisper "All is well".

Ivy Mawby

79 - How Much More

Andante con espress. ♩ = 66

JOHN LARSSON

1. If hu-man hearts are of-ten ten-der, ____ And hu-man minds can pi-ty know, ____ If hu-man love is touch'd with splen-dour, ____ And hu-man hands ____ com-pas-sion show:

CHORUS

Then how much more shall God our Fa-ther ____ In love for-give, ____ in love for-give (for-give).

Then how much more shall God our Fa-ther ____ Our wants sup-ply, and none de-ny. ____

2. If sometimes men can live for others,
   And sometimes give where gifts are spurned,
   If sometimes treat their foes as brothers,
   And love where love is not returned:

3. If men will often share their gladness,
   If men respond when children cry,
   If men can feel each others sadness,
   Each other's tears attempt to dry:

John Gowans

80 - Fellowship

Andante con espress. ♩ = 84

ALBERT DALZIEL

1. "Ye are my friends" said One who was Mas-ter, Shar-ing His King-ly grace with low-ly men;— In that com-mun-ion no sin or dis-ast-er Shall reach the soul, or the spir-it con-demn.

CHORUS Allegro ♩ = 116

'Tis won-der-ful to know the joy that com-eth from a-bove, 'Tis won-der-ful to walk with God in fel-low-ship and love! Though hu-man hopes may

van - ish and earth - ly cares in - crease, _____ 'Tis

rall.

won - der - ful to walk with Him in con - fi - dence and peace.

2. Where can I find a strength all-sustaining?
   Where in security may I abide?
   How keep my faith in the trial past explaining?
   Surely in Christ is my soul fortified!

3. There is a rest, though hands fail with toiling,
   There is a fellowship for lonely hearts;
   There is a healing for sin's fell despoiling,
   This is the boon that His friendship imparts.

Albert Dalziel

81 - I Know He Cares for Me

ANC

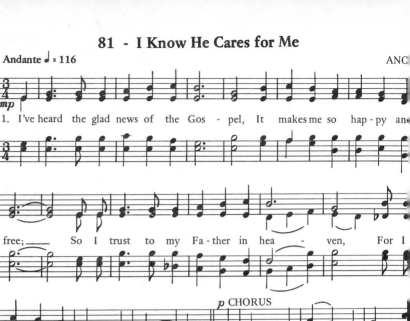

Andante ♩ = 116

1. I've heard the glad news of the Gos - pel, It makes me so hap-py an(d)
free;___ So I trust to my Fa - ther in hea - ven, For I

p CHORUS

know that He cares for me.___ I know He cares for me, fo(r)

cresc. *f*

me; I know He cares for me, for me; I'll trust my

dim. *p*

Fa - ther in hea - ven, for I know that He cares for me.___

2. Sometimes I walk in the darkness,
   My path then I scarcely can see;
   But I trust in my Father in heaven,
   For I know that He cares for me.

3. Sometimes I wish I could see Him,
   And wonder how long it will be;
   But He's gone to prepare me a mansion,
   For I know that He cares for me.

Anon.

82 - Leaning on the Everlasting Arms

Moderato ♩ = 116

ANTHONY J. SHOWALTER

mf

1. What a fel-low-ship, what a joy di-vine, Lean-ing on the ev-er-last-ing arms;— What a bles-sed-ness, what a peace is mine, Lean-ing on the ev-er-last-ing arms.

CHORUS

Lean-ing, Lean-ing, Safe and se-cure from all a-larms;— Lean-ing,— lean-ing, Lean-ing on the ev-er-last-ing arms.

2. O how sweet to walk in this pilgrim way,
   Leaning on the everlasting arms;
   O how bright the path grows from day to day,
   Leaning on the everlasting arms.

3. What have I to dread, what have I to fear?
   Leaning on the everlasting arms;
   I have blessed peace with my Lord so near,
   Leaning on the everlasting arms.

Elisha Hoffman

83 - I'm in His Hands

Andante espressivo ♩= 66

STANLEY DITMA[R]

mf

I shall not fear though dark-ened clouds may ga-ther round me. _____ The God I
(TEN.) The God I

serve is One Who cares and un-der stands. _____ Al - tho' the
(TEN.) Al - tho' the storms,

cresc.

storms I face would threat-en to con-found me, _____ of this I
(BASS) of this _____

f

am as-sured: _____ I'm in His hands (I'm in His hands)!

CHORUS
mp
mp

I'm in His hands, _____ I'm in His hands. _____ What-e'er th[e]
(TEN.) I'm in His hands, _____ I'm in His hands.

cresc.

2. What though I cannot know the way that lies before me,
   I still can trust and freely follow His commands.
   My faith is firm since He it is Who watches o'er me.
   Of this I'm confident: I'm in His hands!

3. In days gone by my Lord has always proved sufficient,
   When I have yielded to the law of love's demands.
   Why should I doubt that He will evermore be present
   To make His will my own? I'm in His hands!

   Stanley Ditmer

84 - Keep on Believing

STEPHEN FOSTER

(Db) Allegretto ♩.= 72

1. When you feel weak - est, dan - gers sur - round,

Sub - tle temp - ta - tions, and trou - bles a - bound, _____

No - thing seems hope - ful, No - thing seems glad,

All is des - pair - ing and ev - 'ry - thing sad. _____

CHORUS

Keep on be - liev - ing, Je - sus is near; Keep on be - liev - ing, there'

no-thing to fear; _____ Keep on be-liev - ing, this is the way;

Faith in the night ____ as well as the day, _____

Faith in the night ____ as well as the day. _____

2. If all were easy, if all were bright,
   Where would the cross be and where would the fight?
   But in the hardness, God gives to you
   Chances of proving that you can be true.

3. God is your wisdom, God is your might,
   God's ever near you and guiding aright;
   He understands you, knows all your need;
   Trusting in Him you will surely succeed.

4. Let us press on then, never despair,
   Live above feeling for victory's there;
   Jesus can keep us so near to Him
   That never more shall our faith become dim.

Lucy Booth-Hellberg

85 - More Than We Can Ask

pro - mised grace for ev - 'ry task; Re - fus - ing to doubt, by
pro - mised grace for ev - 'ry task;

faith___ I reach out, Each pro - mise mine to claim.

2. Though sore temptations often be thy lot,
   He will pray for thee that thy faith fail not;
   Though the raging tempest thou canst not flee,
   His promise still remains: I will strengthen thee.

3. To the meek He promises delight and peace,
   To the over - burdened He will grant release;
   To the upright heart shall true gladness come,
   And prodigals the Father will welcome home.

4. Exceeding precious are the promises
   Which to His true followers our Maker gives,
   And He wills that we may partakers be
   Of blessings stored for us in His treasury.

John Wells

86 - Peace! Be Still

H. R. PALM

Andante ♩.= 60

mf

1 Mas-ter, the tem-pest is rag - ing! The bil-lows are toss-ing high!___

sky is o'er-shad-owed with black-ness, No shel-ter or help is nigh:

Car-est Thou not that we per - ish? How canst Thou lie a - sleep,___

When each mo-ment so mad-ly is threat-'ning A grave in the an-gry deep?___

CHORUS

mp   *p* *dim.*

"The winds and the waves shall o - bey, My will, Peace,___ be still!___
                                                    Peace, be still!   peace, be still!

pp   *cresc. poco a poco*

Whe-ther the wrath of the storm-tossed sea, Or de - mons, or men, or wh

e - ver it be, No wa - ters can swal - low the ship where lies The Mas - ter of o - cean, and earth, and skies: They all shall sweet - ly o - bey My will; Peace, be still! Peace, be still! They all shall sweet - ly o - bey My will; Peace, peace, be still! "

2. Master, with anguish of spirit
   I bow in my grief today;
The depths of my sad heart are troubled,
   Oh, waken and save, I pray!
Torrents of sin and of anguish
   Sweep o'er my sinking soul;
And I perish! I perish! Dear Master:
Oh hasten, and take control.

3. Master, the terror is over,
   The elements sweetly rest,
Earth's sun in the calm lake is mirrored,
   And heaven's within my breast;
Linger, O blessed Redeemer,
   Leave me alone no more;
And with joy I shall make the blest harbour,
   And rest on the blissful shore.

Mary A. Baker

87 - Peace, Perfect Peace

Andante ♩ = 72

ERIK LEIDZEN

1. Peace, per-fect peace, far be-yond all un-der-stand-ing;
Peace, per-fect peace, left with us by Christ, our Lord;
cresc. Peace, per-fect peace, through e-ter-ni-ties ex-pand-ing;
Peace, per-fect peace! Peace, per-fect peace!
(peace, per-fect)

2. Peace, perfect peace, in each trial and disaster;
   Peace, perfect peace, fresh and sweet with every dawn;
   Peace, perfect peace, is the greeting of the Master;
   Peace, perfect peace!
   Peace, perfect peace!

3. Peace, perfect peace, though the tempest round me rages;
   Peace, perfect peace, stronger than the powers of hell;
   Peace, perfect peace, still unchanging through the ages;
   Peace, perfect peace!
   Peace, perfect peace!

4. Peace, perfect peace, when at last death shall o'ertake me;
   Peace, perfect peace, shall surround my lowly grave;
   Peace, perfect peace, when the songs of angels wake me;
   Peace, perfect peace!
   Peace, perfect peace!

Erik Leidzen

88 - Some Glad Sweet Day

Moderato con espress. ♩ = 72

ARTHUR S. ARNOTT

1. Oh, how I'd like to see His face, My Lord be-hold-ing;

Oh, how I'd like to take my place, His arms en-fold-ing.

Some day I'll cross old Jor-dan's tide, Some day the gates will op-en

wide, Then I shall at His feet a-bide; My Lord be-hold-ing.

CHORUS

Some day I'll see His bless-ed face,___ Some day I'll see His bless-ed

face, I'll hear the mus-ic of His voice,___ Some glad, sweet day.

2. There on the cross He died for me,
   My soul redeeming;
   Up from the grave He rose for me,,
   My pardon sealing.
   Some day I'll cross old Jordan's tide
   Some day the gates will open wide,
   Then I shall at His feet abide;
   My Lord beholding.

3. O'er all the hills and dales of life,
   With Jesus walking;
   Amidst the noise of earthly strife,
   I hear Him talking.
   Some day I'll cross old Jordan's tide,
   Some day the gates will open wide,
   Then I shall at His feet abide;
   My Lord beholding.

Arthur S. Arnott

89 - Standing on the Promises

Allegretto ♩ = 100

R. KELSO CART[...]

mf
1. Standing on the pro - mis - es of Christ my King, Thro' e - ter - nal a - ges let H[...]

prais - es ring; Glo - ry in the high - est, I will shout and sing,

CHORUS

Stand - ing on the pro - mis - es of God. Stand - ing, stand - ing,

Stand - ing on the pro - mis - es of God my Sa - viour; Stand - ing, —

stand - ing, I'm stand - ing òn the pro - mis - es of God.

2. Standing on the promises that cannot fail,
   When the howling storms of doubt and fear assail,
   By the living word of God I shall prevail,
   Standing on the promises of God.

3. Standing on the promises of Christ the Lord,
   Bound to Him eternally by love's strong cord,
   Overcoming daily with the Spirit's sword,
   Standing on the promises of God.

4. Standing on the promises I cannot fall,
   List'ning ev'ry moment to the Spirit's call,
   Resting in my Saviour as my all in all,
   Standing on the promises of God.

5. Standing on the promises I now can see,
   Perfect, present cleansing in the Blood for [...]
   Standing in the liberty where Christ makes [...]
   Standing on the promises of God.

R. Kelso Carter

90 - The Gifts of Heaven

HENRY SMART
Tune: Bethany

Moderato ♩ = 96

mf

1. Who the child of God shall sev-er from the faith in which he_ stands?

Who shall wound or who shall pluck him From the care-ful Shep-herd's hands?

cresc.

Not dis-tress or per-se-cu-tion, Neith-er per-il or the sword;

f

For in days of tri-bu-la-tion, Shines the glo-ry of the Lord.

2. His abundant grace is given
   To the heart resigned and meek,
Mercy moves the King of Heaven
   To the penitent and weak;
Lowly paths our Lord has taken,
   And He proved by word and deed,
For the lonely and forsaken
   There is grace beyond all need.

3. Faith is not afraid of darkness,
   Hope will triumph over loss,
Love is not afraid of hardness,
   Patience helps to bear the cross;
These are all the gifts of Heaven,
   Beautiful are they and free,
Graces that the Lord has given,
   Oh, that they may shine in me.

4. Works or wealth can never buy them,
   Nor a single grace impart,
God Himself has sanctified them
   In the meek and lowly heart;
All besides is vain endeavour,
   Failure ev'ry work of mine;
Saviour, let Thy grace for ever
   Cleanse and blend my will with Thine.

Albert Orsborn

91 - When we all get to Heaven

Allegro con spirito ♩ = 116

EMILY WILSON

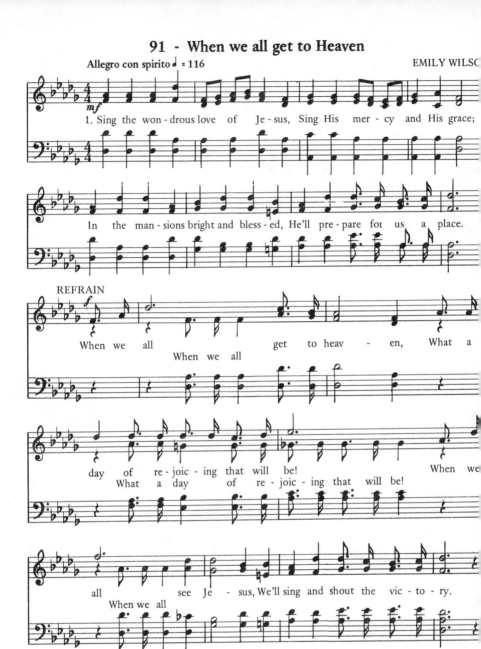

mf

1. Sing the won-drous love of Je-sus, Sing His mer-cy and His grace;

In the man-sions bright and bless-ed, He'll pre-pare for us a place.

REFRAIN

When we all get to heav-en, What a
When we all

day of re-joic-ing that will be! When we
What a day of re-joic-ing that will be!

all see Je-sus, We'll sing and shout the vic-to-ry.
When we all

2. While we walk this pilgrim pathway,
   Clouds may over-spread the sky;
   But when travelling days are over,
   Not a shadow, not a sigh.

3. Let us then be true and faithful,
   Trusting, serving every day;
   Just one glimpse of Him in glory
   Will the toils of life repay.

4. Onward to the prize before us,
   Soon His beauty we'll behold;
   Soon the pearly gates will open,
   We shall tread the streets of gold.

Eliza Hewitt

92 - Bound for the Promised Land

Allegro ♩ = 112

Old American Tune

mf

On Jor - dan's stor - my banks I stand, And cast a wist - ful eye To Ca - naan's fair and hap - py land, Where my pos - ses - sions lie.

f CHORUS

I am bound for the prom - ised land, _____ I'm bound for the prom - ised land; Oh, ___ who will come and go with me? I am bound for the prom - ised land.

2. The bright, transporting, rapturous scene,
   That rises to my sight,
   Sweet fields arrayed in living green,
   And rivers of delight.

3. There generous fruits that never fail,
   On trees immortal grow;
   There rocks and hills, and brooks and vales,
   With milk and honey flow.

4. O'er all those wide extended plains
   Shines one eternal day;
   There God, the Son, forever reigns,
   And scatters night away.

5. Soon will the Lord my soul prepare
   For joys beyond the sky,
   Where never ceasing music rolls,
   And praises never die.

Samuel Stennett

93 - God's Soldier

JOHN LARSSON

Allegro ♩ = 126
ALL VOICES IN UNISON

1. God's sol-dier march-es as to war, A sol-dier on an a-lien shore, A

continue octaves

sol-dier true, A sol-dier who Will keep the high-est aims in view. God's

sol-dier goes where sin is found; Where e-vil reigns, his bat-tle ground; A

cun-ning foe To o-ver throw And strike for truth a tell-ing blow. ____

loco

CHORUS *HARMONY*

We're going to fill, fill, fill the world with glo-ry; ____ We're going to

smile, smile, smile and not frown! —— We're going to sing, sing, sing the gos - pel

sto - ry! —— We're going to turn the world up - side down!

2. God's soldier has to stand alone,
   Accepting burdens not his own;
   A lonely work he cannot shirk,
   Where dark and deadly dangers lurk.
   God's soldier must courageous be,
   And from his duties never flee,
   For millions wait, Whose need is great,
   And he must not God's plan frustrate.

Harry Read

94 - I'm A Soldier Bound for Glory

Allegretto ♩ = 72

Continental Air

I'm a sol-dier bound for Glo-ry, I'm a sol-dier go-ing home; Come and hear me tell my sto-ry, All who love the Sa-viour, come.

f CHORUS

I love Je-sus, Hal-le-lu-jah! I love Je-sus, yes, I do;— I love Je-sus, He's my Sa-viour, Je-sus smiles and loves me too.

2. I will tell you what induced me
   In the glorious fight to start;
   'Twas the Saviour's loving kindness
   Overcame and won my heart.

3. When I first commenced my warfare,
   Many said: He'll run away;
   But they have all been deceivèd,
   In the fight I am today.

4. I'm a wonder unto many,
   God alone the change has wrought.
   Here I raise my Ebenezer,
   Hither by His help I'm brought.

5. When to death's dark, swelling river,
   Like a warrior I shall come,
   Then I mean to shout salvation!
   And go singing glory! home.

Anon.

95 - The Message of the Flag

Allegro ♩ = 116

WILLIAM PENNICK

1. Would you of our ban-ner know the mean-ing, With it's Yel-low,
Red, and Blue? In the breeze, it's crim-son glo-ry streaming, Waves a mes-sage
grand and true.

f CHORUS

Lift up the Ar-my ban-ner, Blood and Fire,
Blood and Fire, ___ Lift it higher; Lift up the Ar-my ban-ner,
Blood and Fire, For it tells of full Sal-va - tion.

2. Blood red crimson tells of God's salvation,
   Bids us think of Christ who died
   For the sins of every tribe and nation,
   When the blood flowed from His side.

3. Fiery yellow, emblem of the Spirit,
   Leads us back to Pentecost;
   He was sent to plead the Saviour's merit,
   And to help us save the lost.

4. Heavenly blue suggests we may be holy,
   Purified from inbred sin;
   Evil tempers, pride, and worldly folly,
   Nevermore to dwell within.

William Pennick

96 - Mine Eyes Have Seen the Glory

Moderato ♩ = 96

WILLIAM STEFFE

1. Mine eyes have seen the glo - ry of the com - ing of the Lord; He is tramp - ling out the vin - tage where the grapes of wrath are stored; He hath loosed the fate - ful light - ning of His ter - ri - ble swift sword; His truth is march - ing on.

CHORUS

Glo - ry, glo - ry, hal - le - lu - jah!

Glo - ry, glo - ry, hal - le - lu - jah! Glo - ry, glo - ry, hal - le-
lu - jah! His truth is march - ing on.

2. I have seen Him in the watch-fires of a hundred circling camps;
   They have builded Him an altar in the evening dews and damps;
   I have read His righteous sentence by the dim and flaring lamps;
       His day is marching on.

3. He has sounded forth the trumpet that shall never call retreat;
   He is sifting out the hearts of men before His judgment seat;
   Oh, be swift, my soul, to answer Him, be jubilant my feet;
       Our God is marching on.

4. In the beauty of the lilies Christ was born across the sea,
   With a glory in His bosom that transfigures you and me;
   As He died to make men holy, let us live to make men free,
       While God is marching on.

Julia Ward Howe

97 - On We March with the Blood and the Fire

Allegro con spirito ♩ = 116

CHARLES MEHLING

1. The Lord's com - mand to go in - to the world and preach the Gos - pel un - to all, Is just as true to - day as when His first dis - ci - ples heard this migh - ty call; So let us gird our - selves and go to bat - tle 'gainst the pow'rs of sin and wrong; Join the fight for the right, in His ev - er - last - ing might And sing our march - ing song.

CHORUS

On we march with the Blood and the Fire, To the

(BASS) On we march, march, march with the Blood and the Fire, ___

ends of the earth we will go; And the

March, march, march, thro' the earth we will go; ___ And the

Sa - viour's love will be the theme of our song, Be - cause we

Sa - viour's love will be the theme of our song, Be - cause we

1.
love Him so (love Him so).

2.
love Him so (love Him so).

love Him, love Him so, love Him so. love Him, love Him so, love Him so.

2. O'er land and sea the Saviour shows the way to every soul sunk deep in sin;
From Calvary's rugged Cross there flows a stream to make the foulest sinner clean;
We'll fill the ranks and trusting in the God of hosts, to lead our mighty throng;
Join the fight for the right, in His everlasting might and sing our marching song.

3. The victory's sure. We're trusting in the promise of our Saviour, Lord and King;
'Lo, I am with you', keeps us free from doubting; to the heav'ns our praises ring;
The whole wide world shall come beneath the sway of Christ, proclaim it loud and long;
Join the fight for the right, in His everlasting might and sing our marching song.

Charles Mehling

98 - Win the World for God

Allegro con spirito ♩ = 116

DOUGLAS COURT

mf

1. There's an ar - my that's been march - ing, March - ing on - ward through the years; On to vic - tory af - ter vic - tory, O - ver sin, and want, and fears. 'Tis the Ar - my of Sal - va - tion: What a work the Lord has done! Tel - ling out the Gos - pel sto - ry Un - til the world for Christ is won.

cresc.

f

CHORUS *f*

So we will keep our Ar - my march - ing, Ar - ound the world our songs will ring, _____ Till one by one they stop and lis - ten, And one by one claim Christ as King. _____ So come and march with us to Glo - ry, A - long the path the saints have trod, _____ We're going to tell the Gos - pel sto - ry, _____ We're going to win the world for God. _____

2. God has given us a message;
   We must shout it loud and clear,
For it tells of peace and pardon,
   'Tis the message all should hear.
We will tell the waiting thousands,
   As our fathers did before,
Of the joy in serving Jesus,
   A joy that lasts for evermore.

3. So, until we reach that city
   Where the saints, who've gone before,
Wait to see our flag appearing,
   Bringing tens of thousands more.
Let us swell our ranks to greet them,
   Never faltering by the way,
For, the Army of tomorrow
   Depends on what we do today.

Douglas Court

99 - Keep in Step

ALFRED VICKERY

Allegro ♩ = 116

Val - iant sol - dier, march-ing to the fray, Keep in step all the
time. Do not lag, or fal - ter by the way; Keep in step all the
time, You may find the way is long and drear,
Man - y dan - gers may cause you to fear; Do not give in, but
strive and per - se - vere, And keep in step all the time.

CHORUS

Keep in step all the time, Keep in step all the
Keep in step, in step all the time, Keep in step, in

time; Don't fall out and rest for a - while, Fol - low Je - sus

step all the time.

all the way, and smile. Keep in step all the time,

all the way, and smile. Keep in step, in step all the time;

Keep in step all the time; You will find each day your

Keep in step in step all the time;

path - way ea - sy if you keep in step all the time. (all the time.)

2. Valiant soldier, you must not despair,
   Keep in step all the time.
Follow Jesus gladly everywhere,
   Keep in step all the time.
March on bravely o'er the battle-field,
In the mighty conflict never yield,
But trust in Jesus, He's your Guide and Shield,
   So keep in step all the time.

3. Valiant soldier, fighting for the Lord,
   Keep in step all the time.
Don your armour, take your shield and sword,
   Keep in step all the time.
Onward, forward, 'tis the Lord's command,
In the cause of right now take your stand,
Go marching forward to the promised land,
   And keep in step all the time.

Alfred Vickery

100 - O Canada!

Maestoso ♩ = 92

CALIXA LAVALLÉE

We stand on guard, We stand on guard for thee _____

O Can - a - da! We stand on guard ___ for thee.

2. O Canada! Where pines and maples grow,
   Great prairies spread and lordly rivers flow,
   How clear to us thy broad domain,
   From east to western sea!
   Thou land of hope for all who toil!
   Thou true north strong and free!

3. O Canada! beneath thy shining skies
   May stalwart sons and gentle maidens rise;
   To keep thee steadfast through the years
   From east to western sea,
   Our own beloved native land,
   Our true north strong and free.

4. Ruler supreme, who hearest humble prayer,
   Hold our Dominion in Thy loving care.
   Help us to find, O God, in Thee
   A lasting, rich reward,
   As, waiting for the better day,
   We ever stand on guard.

R. Stanley Weir

INDEX

(Bold type indicates title of song; regular type refers to the first line of song)

No.

A Friend I have found 76
A Hymn of Faith 74
A Melody in my heart 33
A Mighty Fortress 17
A never-failing Friend 76
A perfect trust 77
A Prayer 52
A sure hiding place................ 35
All my days 54
All there is of me 55
Amazing Grace 73
Are you seeking joys 28
Arise, my soul, arise.............. 18
At Calvary 19
At peace with my God.............. 56

Beautiful Christ 4
Beautiful Jesus, bright Star 4
Bound for the promised land 92
By the peaceful shores of Galilee ... 59

Casting all your care 78
Channels only 53

Don't assume that God's dismissed 21
Down in the valley with my Saviour...... 68

Earthly pleasures vainly call 64
Eternal God, unchanging 74

Fellowship 80
Follow on 68
Follow thou Me 59
For Thine is the Kingdom 2

God's love is wonderful 36
God's love to me 36
God's soldier 93
Great and Glorious 71
Great is Thy faithfulness 5

Have we not known it? 37
Heaven came down 38
He came right down to me 20
He lifted me...................... 41
He lives 34
He remembers sin no more.......... 37

Higher Ground ....
His love remains the same ....
His saving power ....
How I praise Thee, precious.........
How much more ....

I am amazed.......................
I am praying......................
I believe ....
I cannot tell why He whom angels .....
I know a fount ....
I know He cares ....
I know not why God's wondrous grace ...
I know whom I have believed.........
I serve a risen Saviour ....
I shall not fear, though...........
I stand amazed in the presence........
I walked one day along ....
I walk with the King ....
I want to tell what God has done.......
I was sinking deep in sin ....
I will sing of my Redeemer..........
I would be like Jesus ....
If human hearts are often tender ......
I'm a soldier bound for glory ....
I'm in His hands..................
I'm pressing on the upward way........
In loving kindness Jesus came ....
In my heart there's a gladsome.........
In sorrow I wandered ....
In the love of Jesus ....
In the love of Jesus I have found ......
It was love reached me ....
I've heard the glad news of the........

Jesu', O Jesu' ....
Jesus my Lord will love me ....
Joyful news to all mankind ....
Joyful, joyful we adore Thee ....
Just where He needs me.............

Keep in step ....
Keep on believing.................
Kneeling in penitence.............

Leaning on the everlasting arms ....
Like to a lamb who ....

	No.
rd of my life and God	47
rd make Calvary real to me	62
rd, when the crowd gathered	69
ve lifted me	42
ke me aware of Thee	70
ster, the tempest is raging	86
y Jesus Christ be praised	6
ghty to save	24
ne eyes have seen the glory	96
re than we can ask	85
Jesus, I love Thee	63
Saviour's love	43
w I belong to Jesus	45
t unto us, O Lord	7
anada	100
ove upon a cross impaled	25
hou fairest of ten thousand	10
how I'd like to see His face	88
what a wonderful, wonderful	38
every hill our Saviour dies	26
God's word relying	39
Jordan's stormy banks	92
we march with the Blood and the Fire .	97
e on a day was Christ led forth	27
of my bondage	65
ce! Be still	86
ce, perfect peace	87
se Him! Praise Him!	9
ed Hands of Jesus	27
are you weary?	23
only touched the hem	30
the wondrous love of Jesus	91
ing "Ebenezer"	47
e glad, sweet day	88
t Divine, come as of old	66
ding on the promises	89
g wide the door of your heart	28
e up thy cross	67
aksgiving	8
Fairest of ten thousand	10
gifts of heaven	90

	No.
The God of Abraham praise	11
The greatest of these	58
The Lord's command to go	97
The message of the flag	95
The name of Jesus	12
The ninety and nine	29
The old, old story is true	51
The pathway of duty	75
The song in my heart	48
There are promises within	85
There is mercy in Jesus	31
There is strength in knowing	78
There's a path that's sometimes	75
There's a song that's ringing	48
There's a wonderful story I heard	51
There's an army that's been	98
There were ninety and nine	29
These things I know	32
Thine is the glory	13
This is my Father's world	14
This is what the Lord has done	49
Thou didst give Thyself to me	54
Though centuries have fled away	62
Though in declaring Christ	58
Touch me again, Lord	69
Valiant soldier marching	99
We gather together	15
We have a gospel	50
We worship Thee O Lord of light	16
What a fellowship	82
What can I say to cheer	72
When His love reached me	46
When I ponder o'er the story	77
When morning gilds the skies	6
When we all get to heaven	91
When wondrous words my Lord	20
When you feel weakest	84
Wherein shall a nation glory	8
Who the child of God shall sever	90
Win the world for God	98
Would you of our banner	95
Ye are my friends, said One	80
Years I spent in vanity	19
You may roam through the world	31

METRICAL INDEX

An asterisk (*) indicates that a tune can be used for the metre under which it appears by making a slight adjustment.

LONG METRE   No.
He came right down to me 20
On every hill my Saviour dies 26

DOUBLE LONG METRE
God's soldier 93
Higher ground 60

COMMON METRE
Amazing grace 73
Bound for the promised land 92
I know whom I have believed 40
Spirit Divine 66

DOUBLE COMMON METRE
God's love is wonderful 36

DOUBLE SHORT METRE
This is my Father's world 14

6.4.6.4.6.6.6.4.
A Prayer 52

6.5.6.5.
I Believe 39

6.6.6.6.6.6.
May Jesus Christ be Praised 6

6.6.6.6.8.8.
Arise, my soul arise 18
Not unto us, O Lord 7

7.6.7.6.D. Iambic
A Hymn of Faith 74

7.7.7.7. Double
All my days and all my hours 54

8.8.8.6.
He lifted me 41

8.7.8.7.7.7. Trochaic
A perfect trust 77

8.7.8.7. Trochaic   N
Casting all your care 7
I will sing of my Redeemer . . . .
When we all get to heaven 9

8.7.8.7.D. Trochaic
Channels Only 5
I am praying 6
I'm a soldier bound for glory 9
Joyful, joyful, we adore Thee . . . .
Thanksgiving . . . .
The Fairest of ten thousand 1
The gifts of heaven 9
The pathway of duty 7
Win the World for God 9

8.8.8.8.8.8. Iambic
Lord, make Calvary real to me 6
Make me aware of Thee 7
O Love upon a cross impaled 2

9.8.9.8. Double
How much more 7

10.10.10.10. Dactylic
Beautiful Christ . . . .

10's (6 lines) Iambic
In the love of Jesus 5
Sacred hands of Jesus 2

11.8.11.8. Double
A never-failing Friend 7
* The old, old story is true 5

11.10.11.10. Dactylic
Great is Thy faithfulness . . . .

11.10.11.10. Iambic
* I know a fount . . . .
Just where He needs me . . . .

11.11.11.11.
I walk with the King . . . .
My Jesus I love Thee . . . .

IRREGULAR METRES

(Tunes only available for the words to which they are set)

	No.		No.
melody in my heart	33	My Saviour's love	43
mighty Fortress	17	Now I belong to Jesus	45
sure hiding place	35	O Canada	100
there is of me, Lord	55	On we march with the Blood and the Fire	97
Calvary	19	Out of my bondage	65
peace with my God	56	Peace! Be still	86
llowship	80	Peace, perfect peace	87
llow on	68	Praise Him! Praise Him!	9
llow Thou Me	59	Singing Ebenezer	47
r Thine is the Kingdom	2	Some glad, sweet day	88
eat and Glorious	71	Standing on the Promises	89
aven came down	38	Swing wide the Door of your heart	28
Lives	34	Take up Thy cross	67
remembers sin no more	37	The God of Abraham praise	11
s love remains the same	21	The greatest of these	58
s saving power	30	The message of the flag	95
m amazed	22	The name of Jesus	12
now He cares	81	The ninety and nine	29
ould be like Jesus	64	The song in my heart	48
n in His hands	83	There is mercy in Jesus	31
ep in step	99	These things I know	32
ep on believing	84	Thine is the glory	13
aning on the everlasting arms	82	This is what the Lord has done	49
ve lifted me	42	Touch me again, Lord	69
ghty to save	24	We gather together	15
ne eyes have seen the glory	96	We have a gospel	50
re than we can ask	85	We worship Thee, O Lord of light	16
		When His love reached me	46